Hineni:
Here I Am

Hineni: Here I Am

One Woman's Journey
Through Breast Cancer

Sheri Kay

Printed in the United States of America.

Hineni: Here I Am

ISBN 978-1-4507-9944-7

Published by:
Sheri Kay
706 S. Lake St.
Amherst, OH 44001-2164

First Printing 2011

Dedication

I now truly believe that all things are possible.

This is for you, Mom, for having the strength and courage to walk every step with me, no matter how hard it was or how scared we were.

To the love of my life, Scott, for being my voice of reason, my hero, and for loving me back, today and every day. Thanks for marrying me . . . again.

In special loving memory of Jane, who taught me so many things, including how to live with Cancer.

To all of my doctors, nurses, and healers. Without you, I would not be alive to tell my story.

To all the women and men who have heard or will hear the words, "You have Cancer." More than anything, I want you to remember that you are not alone.

I know my dad would be proud.

Acknowledgments

I now understand what "it takes a village" means, because it has taken a village to make this book become a reality.

Thank you, first and foremost, to my dedicated and loving "virtual community." You were all there for me every step along the way and helped me believe that my message was a worthy one.

I offer my love and appreciation to Cory, Debbie, Ro, Rachael, Kirk, Teryl, Joan, Toto, Barb, Donna, my two Jills, Debbie, Corky, Jo, Mark, Mike & Melissa, Brian & Suzie Q, Kathleen, and Mary Anne.

My editing team is a big one and includes the "Empress" Caro Carson: Midnight Line Editor; my big brother, Arthur Evenchik; and the woman who wouldn't rest until we made it to print, my dear friend Deb Bush.

Special thanks to Xana and the design team at Golden Proportions for your creativity and patience, and to Jane for providing the inspiration for the design.

Thank you to my photographer, David Murphy, for your kindness and patience, especially in those really hard moments. You have been here every single time I called, even when I didn't give you much notice!

Thank you to all my friends, family, and clients for being in my life.

Table of Contents

Prologue

Nobody should have to go through something terrible in order to learn that they are loved. I knew I was loved. And yet, I never would have known just how much or by how many people had it not been for the experiences that you will read about in this book.

The funny thing is, I never actually planned on writing a book.

I'm a Dental Practice Coach, which means that I work with dental practices all across the country building teams and developing relationships that are very important to me. My job keeps me on the road more than 100 days a year, and I love what I get to do.

When I was diagnosed with Breast Cancer in February 2010, one of my biggest concerns was how to stay connected to the people who are so dear to me. I have friends, family, clients, study groups, and colleagues all around the world, and the thought of trying to communicate with everyone was absolutely daunting. I had heard about an online blog where people with illnesses could keep journals and update friends and family on details. It sounded like an easy form of communication. And so, on March 4, 2010, I started writing on www.CaringBridge.org.

It didn't take long before this online forum became an important part of my life. Not only was I able to report on what was happening, but I found the act of writing incredibly meaningful and downright therapeutic as I moved through my surgeries and treatment. I experienced great clarity when I sat at my keyboard and found that I was able to get in touch with what was happening mentally, spiritually, physically, and emotionally. The words just started to flow, and before I knew it, this blog was taking on a life of its own.

My "virtual community" was reading, and they were also responding! Every single day, I received messages of hope and inspiration on the guest pages which moved me and motivated me to write even more. At some point, I realized that I was even getting messages from strangers who found my story somehow helpful in their lives. And then, the most important thing happened: three different women I knew phoned to tell me that they had just been diagnosed with Breast Cancer. By coincidence, they had been reading my blog, and they told me that they found it extremely helpful.

I had been writing for months, describing the details of my surgeries and what it was like to prepare for and go through Chemo. I had spoken of my fears and successes and my tears and my triumphs, and other women were finding hope for themselves within the words of my stories. Over and over I kept hearing people say that this blog "should become a book."

My CaringBridge site continued to be a source of inspiration, information, and hope for many other women, and so I decided to "make it happen." There were a handful of very special angels in my life who had walked the big walk through Cancer before me and who had helped, guided, loved, and supported me on my journey. This is my way of "paying it forward" in the best way I know how—being there for other women facing similar challenges in their lives.

So here it is . . . the book I never planned to write.

Chapter 1
How Did This Thing Start?

Thursday, March 4, 2010

It feels crazy to even have a reason to create an online journal for myself ... yet here I am beginning to write my "story," and here you are caring enough to stop by and read.

I'm sure by now you know that I was diagnosed with Breast Cancer. I have had numerous biopsies in the past couple of years, and this time the event was more than a simple inconvenience in my week. Here it is, just over two weeks later, and everything seems to be moving in high-speed motion as I prepare for a double mastectomy and beginning reconstruction on Tuesday, March 9.

What you may not know is that I received my diagnosis while I was on my mission trip to Guatemala with LAMP, Latin American Medical Providers—the greatest group of people in the world, dedicated to providing access to medical and dental care for the people in the Jalapa area ... I digress, sorry. So many people are feeling so bad that I "found out" while I was out of the country, and I want to assure you that I was in exactly the best possible place for me. When my husband, Scott, told me that he had the results, I was able to immediately create a support network within my community there. I couldn't have asked for a more caring, concerned, or supportive environment to be in. I had space to cry, get hugs, have great conversations, and receive professional guidance from nurses, surgeons, friends, and even other Breast Cancer survivors.

But the most important part of being there was that I got to turn my attention and focus back to the most amazing people: the patients I was there to serve. The days were long, working conditions fair, toilets gross, and food ... well, not my favorite. And yet, I felt absolutely capable, alive, productive, and appreciated every single moment of every single day. Our team helped hundreds and hundreds of folks who have very little, if any, access to care, and these patients thanked us, hugged us, brought us gifts, and prayed for us every day. It was pretty hard to sit there and feel bad about an early diagnosis, knowing I would be in the midst of the Cleveland Clinic health system within days of coming back to my home country. I had and am still having a hard time reconciling the disparity between what I was witnessing there and what I would be experiencing here in terms of care. We are truly blessed.

So, after visits with my surgeon and plastic surgeon, the plan is to move forward as quickly as possible. My initial desire was to hold off as long as possible so that I could complete the work commitments I had ahead of me. Wow, did I get slammed on that one! I am still hearing the words *loudly* in my head from my dear friend and boss, Kirk, as he continued to remind me that "life comes first," and that our clients would be both understanding and supportive. As soon as I really took in what Kirk was saying, I realized just how right he was. Yesterday, I finished working with an amazing new team in Fargo, North Dakota, and my entire focus now is preparing for my procedures and my recovery.

I am very nervous about what lies ahead, especially not yet knowing whether or not I will need Chemo. I have no concept of how much pain I will have or how challenging recovery will be. I do know there is at least one more surgery following this one, and possibly more. I'm hoping I can get to my computer and my phone within a matter of days! In the meantime, I will be asking Scott and my dear friend Rachael to keep you posted through this online journal.

For now, I appreciate your thoughts, prayers, cards, and calls. And I hope this site provides a great forum for all of us to be and stay connected while I take this little "vacation."

> With much love and gratitude,
> Sheri

Chapter Two
Who Picks These Lessons?

Friday, March 5, 2010 10:47 PM, EST

Scott and I saw my plastic surgeon again today for my final consult and reviewed what will happen on Tuesday. I keep asking questions and am being told "it depends" pretty much at every turn. I'm doing my best to focus on what is certain and constant, and then I can breathe again.

I'm certain that my choice to have a double mastectomy is the right one.

I'm certain that I have chosen talented, caring, and well-respected surgeons.

I'm certain that I will feel as though I've been run over by at least one truck, and I hear the bruising is going to be phenomenal. If the colors are noteworthy, I will see about posting pictures.

I'm certain that I am surrounded by people who love me, and trust that I will be perfectly cared for when I return home.

A special thanks goes out tonight to an ex-patient of mine from one of my dental practices. He is a radiologist in the hospital where I will be having my surgery, and he has agreed to perform the injections for the sentinel node biopsy. I have been crazy with anxiety about this procedure, and knowing that he will be doing it has made a huge and wonderful difference in my mindset.

I'm really doing my best to control, or at least influence, what I can when I can. Letting go and trusting the rest is certainly where my work is right now.

Saturday, March 6, 2010 10:37 AM, EST

In the wee hours of this morning as the sun began to rise, my Spirit was dancing in that wondrous place between sleep and awake.

It was then I realized that something quite magical had occurred over the past couple of days . . . that time, space, and distance had completely collapsed . . . for how else could I be completely surrounded by all of you?

I looked around slowly and found that I could clearly see your faces, hear all of your voices, and experience your presence. In that same moment I realized that I could physically feel your warmth, your touch, your arms around me . . . and then I realized that I was not merely being held . . .

My tears began to flow, and my body relaxed . . . so gently, so softly, so intentionally and so lovingly, you each began to lift me. You lifted me to the place where I could feel safe, beyond this earth plane where fear and pain have threatened to be greater than the faith and hope that live deep inside.

And that, my dear friends, is how I awoke on Wednesday morning. I am humbled by your kind words, your inspiration, your "virtual gifts," and your presence in this most challenging time.

Three more days . . . and yes, I'm counting.

Saturday, March 6, 2010 11:27 PM, EST

Scott has been building us an exercise room for the past couple of months, and today he began the finishing touches . . . like getting the paint on the walls! It's impossible to feel anything but happy when I walk into this very bright orange room with tons of natural light, bright white crown molding, and beautiful new carpet. Pretty soon we will move in the cardio stuff and have our new universal equipment delivered.

Sounds bittersweet, doesn't it? We've been talking about doing this for years, and just as it so beautifully gets completed I will be heading into surgery, with no idea about when I will be able to start working out again.

But here's the deal. I'm already picturing myself walking on the treadmill, and slowly working my way back on the bike. Finally, they will tell me that it's time to work my upper body, and I will only have to walk through the kitchen to begin my own rehab and strength building.

Timing perfect? You bet.

I learned many years ago in dentistry how important it is to begin any project with the end in mind. *I'm listening to all you guys* and I clearly see myself as healthy, free of Cancer, and in the best shape of my life. (Even if I have to have a little help with that "shape.")

Love to you all,
Sheri

Sunday, March 7, 2010 11:07 PM, EST

So much has been happening on the "strategic" side of this process with surgeon and plastic surgeon appointments, doing research on what to expect by spending crazy amounts of time on the Internet, learning everything possible just so I could know at least what questions to keep asking. Whew!

Tonight marked the beginning of my getting ready on the spiritual and energetic sides of this walk I'm about to take. Our new exercise room in all its orange glory became the chapel for us to light my Hope candle, do some drumming and chanting, and offer some prayers. The music was magical tonight, and together our circle found numerous rhythms of life, celebration, and reflection.

I found myself very teary this morning, and I couldn't figure out why my eyes were leaking so much. But crap, it's so easy to get scared about the invasiveness and the pain and uncertainty of so much. It feels good to cry and release some of the pressure!

Visiting with friends and family all day and all evening was perfect. I head off to sleep thinking about tomorrow . . . and then it will be just one more day. Sleep well, my friends.

Monday, March 8, 2010 3:49 PM, EST

So, bright and early this morning Scott and I were off to the final plastic surgery appointment. (By the way, Scott has been with me for every appointment in the past two weeks.) I left the office with all the surgical markings for tomorrow. What this means is that I have more ink on my chest than my kid (with all his tattoos) has on his whole body—and that is a lot of ink. In some ways, it feels really odd, kinda like having someone paint a target on my body and knowing that a trigger is about to be pulled. Don't get me wrong—I really don't feel like I'm about to die. It's just that we are right back to the strategic part, and that is the part that is so cold and unnerving.

In about an hour, I will be in the caring and healing hands of a couple of friends who offered to come by and do a Reiki session. This will help me relax and "get into my body" in preparation for tomorrow and beyond. My ability to stay calm, focused, and present feels super important right now. I am aware of my anxiety rising and falling, and I am doing what I can to at least make sure I continue to breathe. I had two breathing lessons yesterday (yes, I

Nothing means more to me than having your love and prayers, so please know that I, too, will be sitting in the quiet, waiting to go to surgery, and focusing on all things good, healthy, and healed, along with anyone else who is present across the globe.

actually have friends who teach breathing), and so I am doing my best to practice what I learned. Oh, and in case you're wondering, we will be back in the orange room for my Reiki session. Have I mentioned how much I love this room?

This will most likely be my last communication of the day, and I do want you to know that a dear friend has organized an international prayer circle for 7:30 EST tomorrow morning. Nothing means more to me than having your love and prayers, so please know that I, too, will be sitting in the quiet, waiting to go to surgery, and focusing on all things good, healthy, and healed, along with anyone else who is present across the globe.

I continue to be in awe over the cards, calls, Skypes, emails, texts, messages, flowers, and every other possible way that so many people have made sure that I know they are right here with me.

The time I need to be at the hospital has changed, so if you happen to roll over at 5 a.m. and look at your clock, please know that I am almost at the hospital. Surgery time is 9:30.

The next entry you see will most likely be from Rachael (sometime tomorrow) after she has a post-op report from my handsome husband.

> Love to you,
> Sheri

Tuesday, March 9, 2010 5:06 PM, EST

Hello, Everyone. Rachael here. I just got off the phone with Sheri. Surgery went well, and she is tucked in her room now. She says she feels pretty good (of course, she is on lots of pain meds!). She will stay in the hospital overnight and be back home tomorrow. As soon as she is up to it, she will be back here posting. Thank you for all of your prayers!

Tuesday, March 9, 2010 8:13 PM, EST

Hi all—it's Rachael here again. I just spoke with Sheri and she is doing well. She seems relatively comfortable, and the meds are still working—not in much pain. She was incredibly touched by how many of you have checked the site (200 today alone!) and left her messages. If you know Sheri, you know that being part of a supportive and caring community is the best medicine ever. It really does mean the world to her. Kudos to you all for giving Sheri lots to smile about!

Wednesday, March 10, 2010 10:55 AM, EST

Rachael here. Sheri is having a few routine tests done today and is on track to be released from the hospital late this afternoon. She slept pretty well last night and feels okay other than some pain when she lifts her arms, which is to be expected. All in all, she's doing well and continues to be amazed at the massive outpouring of love and support she is receiving from all of you. She hasn't been on the computer, but Scott has been reading her your entries from time to time. If any new news pops up today, I will let you know. Otherwise, I expect that the next Journal entry you read will be from Sheri herself!

Wednesday, March 10, 2010 7:10 PM, EST

I did it! I did it! And I made it home about 5:30 in the evening. In the process, I unfortunately managed to get behind the pain a bit. I will do my best not to let that happen again. There was just too much of a time lag between leaving the hospital, getting to my post-op appointment with the plastic surgeon, and then getting home. Drugs are good. Naps are good, too.

The surgeon is very happy with how I look 24 hours post-op, but I have to tell you my feelings are quite different. It was harder than I realized it would be to look down as he removed the bandages and witness for the first time the mass destruction that has just occurred to my body. The incision on the left side is about seven inches long and the right about four. Even though I did know how big they would be and I did laugh about the surgical markings, the reality is quite sobering.

Seems there was lymph node involvement, and I will find out on Monday exactly what that means. For now, my understanding is that I will need to undergo Chemo, and my physical experience is some pain and numbness running down the back of my left arm and along and past my elbow. Not sure if this is temporary, but that is certainly my hope.

So, my friends, it is an extra good day for me to be sitting here, reading your posts and reminding myself that whatever I am feeling in this moment will be better in the next. I really was hoping that my treatment would end with this surgical intervention. It looks like I'll be digging a little deeper and jumping through a few more hoops. Thanks for continuing to remind me that I can indeed "do this."

> So, my friends, it is an extra good day for me to be sitting here, reading your posts and reminding myself that whatever I am feeling in this moment will be better in the next.

Love to you,
Sheri

Thursday, March 11, 2010 3:02 PM, EST

The other day I made a wish that it were spring so that I could work on recovery from my new back patio. Seems the universe granted my wish, as I've been outside twice today, soaking up the sun and enjoying the very fresh air.

My only complaint today is that I continue to get the hiccups, of all things. Very intense and very close together, and my poor chest has already been pretty abused. I'm not sure what started this, but I am ready to have it be done.

My very special women's circle has begun to convene. How cool is it that we made plans eight months ago for our gathering to be in Oberlin, Ohio, this weekend? There are eight of "us" from around the country: Washington, Oregon, Indiana, New Hampshire, Georgia, Texas, and of course, Ohio. My soul sisters are gently coming to visit and have created all kinds of rules for me to follow so that I don't overdo or get overtired. I guess the plan is that one or two will come at a time, so it's like I will be allowed to have them in shifts. Part of me was sad about not being able to be with the whole group, but the bigger part of me is filled with joy to have them right around the corner, even in shifts, for the next few days.

Time for another nap. 'Bye for now!

Friday, March 12, 2010 8:11 AM, EST

They might not let me work,
but even in recovery I can wear
my company apparel.

Sorry the sun isn't shining this morning, but at least you can see me up and out.

I made it into our waterbed last night for the first time (you can laugh if you want, but I love my waterbed), and Scott and I had a good laugh trying to figure out how to get me out of it this morning. Very slowly, I am able to use my arms, so at least I could push a little while he made sure I didn't fall head over heels forward. What can I say?

Everybody has their own set of unique challenges each and every day. The only difference is that I am living mine out loud right now.

I don't remember if I told you about having a body scan in the hospital the other day. They scanned my chest, abdomen, and pelvis. Today I will get another IV of radioactive dye, hang around the hospital for three hours, and then have a bone scan performed. I hope this means that when I meet with my surgeon on Monday, I will learn about the surgical pathology report, be referred to oncology for a Chemo treatment plan, and also hear that all other scans were negative. As I know prayers are still coming . . . a clean rest of my body would be a great image to hold.

As I know prayers are still coming . . . a clean rest of my body would be a great image to hold.

My other visit is back to my plastic surgeon. I think I will be able to say good-bye to two out of three drains and get the bandages off. This could mean a real shower today, so I'm crossing my fingers. The swelling is down a lot, although my left arm is still dancing between being in a lot of pain and feeling numb from below my elbow all the way up. I guess this is from the lymph node dissection, and rumors say it is temporary.

All in all, my dear friends, I'm moving right along. Have a great day!

P.S. Hiccups are much better! Thanks for the tips.

My women's
circle, all
around me

Me? Break rules? Hee hee . . . just once in a while. I knew there would be
a three-hour interim between the radioactive injection and the bone
scan yesterday. What I didn't know was that they would let me leave the
hospital. I obviously had two choices: go home and rest, or go find my
girlfriends at the bed & breakfast in Oberlin. No-brainer, and my choice
came with an added bonus.

When I arrived, the owner of the B&B was just about to go for a walk.
When Marcia saw me, she instead stayed and we had a wonderful visit.
Marcia is an oncology nurse in Elyria, and while we waited for everyone
to return from their walk, she was able to help me understand a lot
about what to expect and what questions to ask around Chemo. It was
crazy to hear how much things have changed and how much better this
whole process has become in the past few decades.

I was quite the surprise package for the six ladies who had already
shown up, and we did have a wonderful visit for almost two hours
before I needed to go back for my scan. As much as I love attention, even
I can have a hard time with too much on me in any given moment . . .
but not with this group! Within minutes I had hugs and a foot massage
going, gifts coming to me, and stories being told and read. The amount
of "raw woman energy" surrounding me helped me feel more whole and
more real in some magical way.

Although there is one person left to come in from Texas, it was a perfect entry to my group.

Today I do feel good enough to go over and spend some time with them in sacred space, and I joyfully will show up as number eight to complete this circle for the first time this weekend. And who thought I could only have visitors in shifts?

Before I sign off, I want you all to know that I have not taken any pain meds since the night before last. Ibuprofen has been plenty good for the small amount of this or that here and there that I feel. I know I can be quite entertaining on meds, but I certainly prefer to be awake and present any day.

Hugs,
Sheri

Sunday, March 14, 2010 8:09 AM, EDT

My sister made me laugh yesterday when she said that reading my postings is like watching *The Truman Show*. Each day, she enjoys seeing what's happening on my end. I must say that it has been quite therapeutic for me to get what is happening captured in this way, and it's a bonus to know that folks are enjoying my bantering.

Today's bigger post will come a little later today. I need to get moving and go for our "closing session" with my group. I've threatened to hold them all hostage, but it seems they all have lives "back home" to attend to.

Until later, my friends,
Sheri

Sunday, March 14, 2010 8:42 PM, EDT

Waking up this morning, I was already in tears. Although my left arm pain from the lymph node dissection had kept me awake, I was filled with an overwhelming sense of love and gratitude for Scott and everything he is doing for me, but then I felt very sad thinking about my friends leaving.

It was a special and magical few days of community, learning, loving, and adapting to the ever-changing plans of what we thought could happen and what was really possible. The reality of Cancer making its uninvited entrance into our sacred circle was both manageable and acceptable and at the same time painfully unbearable. We all fell into our stories and found amazing ways to allow, console, accept, embrace, and unfold the layers that each of us unraveled, stories both related and unrelated to what is happening for me.

I'm not naive enough to believe that my experience is only impacting me. My process is like a giant conduit for so many people to sit in their own challenges and fears. This weekend we all found a way to put language and voice to what was present. The greatest gift that the group gave me was their willingness to let me "show up" in a constant dance that shifted from "Breast Cancer warrior" to the scared and innocent child wanting to wake up from a bad dream.

It takes great courage to sit and be a witness to anyone in a challenging process. I learned this first in dentistry and then in each and every relationship in my life. Of all the things I am grateful for, the people who are willing to really be in this with me mean the most.

> Of all the things I am grateful for, the people who are willing to really be in this with me mean the most.

With the good-bye and the ending of this session, it feels as though a huge chapter is being closed. This chapter could have been called "Preparing and Physically Healing from Surgery Number One." We wrote that chapter with grace and a few significant scars. It's beginning the next chapter that feels most scary: "What Comes Next? and How to Spell C-H-E-M-O." If I am certain of at least one lesson right now, it is about embracing ambiguity and completely letting go of making any plans. Talk about the antithesis of how I usually live my life!

Who picks these lessons, anyway?

Lastly, I sit and think about what it means to heal. For today, I leave you knowing that my desire to be on the other side of this is incredibly greater than my fear of what it will take to get there.

Thanks to all of you who are sending flowers and gifts and bringing food. I continue to feel completely surrounded by pure love, and my house smells wonderful.

just me

Chapter Three
How to Spell C-H-E-M-O

Monday, March 15, 2010 8:20 PM, EDT

Thanks to the daylight savings time change, I feel like today has been about ten minutes long. Crazy, though, 'cause we also packed a ton of things in. I am so happy to tell you that all reports could not have been better.

Doctor Visit Number One with my plastic surgeon:

Drains are out, sutures removed, and he said that I am the new successor to a Breast Cancer patient of years gone by who had the best attitude he had ever witnessed. Yes! I really feel like I've won an award. This guy is wonderful, but hasn't previously been too personal and not at all effusive. This was quite the compliment.

Doctor Visit Number Two with my general surgeon:

I was getting my pathology report in the hallway because he was too excited to wait for me to get in the exam room. The news was the best possible! We knew there was Cancer in the sentinel node on the day of surgery. As a result, they removed sixteen additional nodes, and they all came back negative for more Cancer. Yay! As I expected, there were pre-cancerous cells in my right breast, affirming for me my decision to have the double mastectomy.

We talked a lot about my left arm and the pain/numbness that I am experiencing. We are all optimistic that this is mostly temporary, but only time will tell just how much the affected nerves will recover. I now have some exercises to do and feel confident that even without full recovery, this will become more tolerable.

Other great news is that both my body scan and my bone scan are clean. Whew!

Conclusion, no more surgeries—other than completing my reconstruction.

Visit Number Three with my oncology nurse:

Even though my actual doctor appointment with oncology is not until tomorrow morning at 9, I had a great conversation with the nurse in that department this morning. She was awesome and invited me to come up and meet her, tour the infusion suites, and ask my preliminary questions. In twenty minutes, she was able to alleviate the majority of my fears, and I know I will sleep better tonight thanks to her gift of time and caring.

My biggest questions around Chemo should be answered in the morning. When to start? What is the treatment? How often? How bad will the nausea be? Will I lose my hair? (I think the answer is yes.) What is the duration? These questions are getting easier to ask as the answers become less frightening.

Oh, I also learned that I will be able to travel during treatment, so it is very realistic to create a plan to get back on the road, visiting my dental teams and resuming my coaching. (This part makes me smile really big.)

Visit Number Four:

A date with my couch. It's not surprising how this day of celebration completely wore me out. With my favorite meditation music, I was down for the count.

Visit Number Five with my friend and gifted healer, Maha:

My community of Lightworkers holds many talented women who are more than happy to show up and do some bodywork with me— especially once they see the "orange room." Bodywork is almost like a massage, but you keep your clothes on and the "work" is done on the energetic level of the body and soul. Maha was able to really calm my body and my Spirit and help me regain some much-needed grounding. It's harder than you can imagine to stay in my body with so much happening. Although there is a healthy perspective to experiencing a lot of this as an observer rather than a participant, my preference is to stay present. Maha was able to help me do just that, become centered and present.

Success for me continues to be finding the balance between those strategic and spiritual components. Today was indeed a success.

Hugs,
Sheri

Tuesday, March 16, 2010 6:59 PM, EDT

Another giant big day, my friends, and today it was all about the appointment with my oncologist first thing this morning.

Let me assure you that all the good news of yesterday still stands as being really good news. The twist is that based on what we learned yesterday, I made the mistake of making some assumptions about what my Chemo plan would be like. You know what they say about assumptions. Oops . . .

The story I told myself was that I wouldn't have to be very aggressive with my Chemo, since all the reports were so good. What I did not realize is that my pathology report indicates that "my Cancer" is highly invasive and aggressive, so we need to be very proactive in killing whatever little Cancer seeds are floating around in my body. (Okay, this may not be the most scientific description you'll ever get, but this is how I understand it all works.)

My appointment was almost two hours long, and we covered a lot of territory in terms of information and planning.

Long story short:

I will begin Chemo on April 22. There will be two different "cocktails," each one lasting for four treatments over an eight-week period. This is a total of eight treatments happening every two weeks for sixteen weeks. Each treatment is two days, with the first day being a long infusion for three-and-a-half hours, and the second day, a quick injection.

Every treatment is preceded by a blood test to ensure that my blood cell counts are high enough to continue. The hope is that we can get this started, stay on course, and "get 'er done."

20

The week prior to the first treatment, my surgeon will be placing a port in the upper part of my chest so that the doctors will have "permanent" access both to draw blood and to administer the infusions along with any other medications that would normally go through an IV. This is a short outpatient procedure, and I think it sounds way worse than it is. (According to the online videos, it's not a big deal at all.)

The big question that everybody is asking is about hair loss, and I was definitively told today that yes, I will be losing my hair. I'm not excited, but quite frankly, being assured that they can manage nausea feels way more important to me than whether or not I need to wear a hat. I know it will be very hard to lose my hair and even harder in many ways for the people around me to witness me with no hair. And . . . it will grow back. That is one thing that I can absolutely count on. It will grow back. Now I have to admit that at a time like this, I wish I looked like Halle Berry or Sharon Stone! I will do my best not to scare anyone, and maybe somebody will offer lessons on how to be super cool with scarf tying.

I had very fun visits today from dear friends (there are now prayer ties hanging in my trees) and I enjoyed being outside with my mom for a good dose of sunshine and fresh air. Then more friends came by with hugs and dinner, and I could feel the wind coming back in my sails.

Although you are hearing this over and over . . . if it were not for everyone (all of you) surrounding me in different ways, this process would be virtually unbearable. Thank you for helping me feel so cared for and loved. You continue to remind me how to keep going even when it feels really hard.

> Hugs,
> Sheri

Wednesday, March 17, 2010 7:22 PM, EDT

What a joy to wake up this morning and not have any appointments to go to. I showered, dried my hair (that was actually my big accomplishment for the day, with my left arm doing better), and then put my PJ's back on. Can you see me smiling?

My day was filled with a couple of early-day visitors, some time on the patio, and a number of client calls to at least get me a little bit back in the coaching saddle. It feels so good to focus on something other than learning about Chemo for a while. I am energized to be back in the "work world," where I can feel informed and competent, where I have some of the answers to other people's questions, and *all of the language is perfectly comfortable and familiar.*

I am, by nature, a learner. Learning is like breathing to me. I live to stimulate and satisfy my curiosity about millions of things. Wanna talk about Coaching? Dentistry? Philosophy? Spirituality? Dentistry? Systems? Bicycles? Dentistry? Relationships? Fitness? Shopping? The Orange Room? It's fun to explore what is known, not known, hypothesized, and theorized.

And now I am learning about something that I didn't know I wanted to know about. My mom said to me yesterday, "Boy, we are learning a lot," and yes, we are. It started with mammograms, ultrasounds, and imaging classifications. Then we moved up to biopsies and pathology. Surgery and plastics came next, with a bonus chapter on placing ports and designing Chemo plans. Who'd a thunk? All I can think about is how important it is to learn everything I can . . . and then my head feels full . . . and then I am so happy to return to the place where *I know the language and it is comfortable and familiar.*

One of my great blessings is that my work is actually one of the places where I can be whole, where I can heal, where I can continue to make a positive difference. So if you happen to call and I can't "talk right now," please know that I am probably busy doing something I love.

It was a good day.

Lastly, I may or may not continue daily posts, as much of the "strategic stuff" is on pause for a bit. I do reserve the right to offer some musings as my creative juices allow.

In love and gratitude,
Sheri

Saturday, March 20, 2010 10:13 AM, EDT

I know all my lady friends will get this one: imagine putting on an underwire bra that is a full size too small. You can feel it pulling very tight across the front, and the underwires are pressing way too hard across the top of your rib cage. That is pretty much what I've been feeling for the past few days, as I'm healing and getting more in touch with different sensations. The only big difference between my analogy and reality is that I could take it off if it were a damn bra.

I keep hearing people remind me that I am only so many days post-op (today is eleven), and I really am doing quite well. But yesterday I was crawling out of my skin with this "tightness." So I did what any woman in 2010 would do, and spent the rest of my day and evening learning everything I could on the Internet about post-mastectomies, expanders, filling expanders, removing expanders, complications of expanders, just to name a few.

If we haven't talked about this yet, the expanders are like empty implants that have been placed behind my chest muscles. The plastic surgeon inserted them on mastectomy day and "filled" them with 75cc of saline to give me at least a little bit of boobage right out of the gate. The expanders have ports (beneath the skin, so I can't see them) where more saline can be injected over time. The whole process is designed to stretch my skin and basically grow breasts (nipples not included—another conversation for later). When we attain a size that is acceptable, the surgeon will over-expand them just a bit and then schedule another surgery, where the expanders are exchanged for long-term implants.

Keep in mind that surgery cannot happen until at least a month after completion of Chemo. My Chemo does not start for five weeks, and my course is a total of sixteen weeks, barring any complications or delays. Now can you see why I started having so many questions? All of a sudden it hit me that these expanders are going to be in place for a very, very long time. I mean, best-case scenario is second surgery in October! This is the first day of spring, so I have two full seasons to go. My trees are still bare from winter, and these underwires will be here until the leaves are falling off again. Okay, Sheri, just b r e a t h e.

Scott, my resident caregiver and knower of all, assures me that once they fill these suckers a little more, they will become more comfortable. I have to tell you, it seems like having them filled will be the opposite of "more comfortable." In fact, the only posts on the Internet are the ones where women feel as if their chest is going to explode and they are screaming in pain, asking for the expanders to come out. Realistically, I have to believe that I will feel a bit stretched for a few days, and then hopefully the underwire feeling will lessen as the expander gets more full. Since my first fill appointment is just about a week away, I will let you know.

For now, I will offer you information that is very different from that on the Internet: I have very little pain. The expanders are not fun, but very tolerable. I don't have any bras that fit, but it doesn't matter, 'cause I don't need one.

FYI, my Internet search yesterday also involved many more topics, like Chemo side effects and especially dealing with hair loss.

More to come in my next post.

Hugs,
Sheri

Monday, March 22, 2010 5:33 PM, EDT

Gratitude unlocks the fullness of life. It turns what we have into enough, and more. It turns denial into acceptance, chaos to order, confusion to clarity. It can turn a meal into a feast, a house into a home, a stranger into a friend. Gratitude makes sense of our past, brings peace for today, and creates a vision for tomorrow. —Melody Beattie

There is so little that any of us have any control over, and this thing called Cancer seems to magnify the extent of just how great our "illusion of control" is. We think we can plan. We think we can prepare. And then, out of the blue, the Universe has a different idea about what will happen next. It's in that moment that each one of us has a choice.

How will I respond? This has become the most important question for me to ask myself throughout each moment of every day.

This whole hair loss thing is quite the mind-f@#k, pardon my French. I am telling you one minute that I really have come to terms with what will happen, and the next minute I find myself looking in the mirror, trying to imagine what I'm going to look like. I pull my hair back and play with a hat or scarf, making up ways to make knots that don't work. Will I keep my eyebrows and my eyelashes? Then I squint my eyes really tight and try to see me without those, too. Oh, yeah, the question . . . How will I respond?

In my effort to find at least some things that I can influence, I decided to cut a bunch of my hair off and begin to explore some wig options. I figure it will be easier to lose my hair a bit at a time instead of all at once at the will of my upcoming Chemotherapy. I like this idea! I can feel good about this. So Saturday felt like a big day. I had made the appointment and "my girl" had agreed to see me after hours, so we could have some privacy trying on wigs.

The wig thing didn't work out too well. Seems the whole Cancer problem is a local epidemic, so the inventory of wigs was quite depleted. (They gave away four just this past week. Scary, isn't it?) So we focused on the haircut. I am no stranger to short hair, although it's been a while since I chose this route. It was quite cathartic to watch the long pieces fall to the floor as Karen and I laughed about *American Idol* and other equally important life issues. In many ways it felt like any other visit to my salon. After all, it was just a haircut, right?

Since it was getting late and the shop was officially closed, I offered to go ahead and pay, so that the girl at the desk could close her drawer. Karen paused and let me know that there would be no fee for the cut. I felt my breath get caught in my throat and the tears began to flow. All I could say was, "I don't want a pity cut," with what probably sounded like the voice of a child.

Karen gently and softly assured me that this was just the opposite, a gesture to a friend, a way to show love and support. We both cried for a moment or two before we found our way back to *Grey's Anatomy* and *Private Practice*, other important components of a changing life.

I love my new short little cut, and it took me less than a minute to get it ready for my day. I continue to be humbled by the many ways that so many people are offering their own versions of what love, support, and kindness can be.

> I continue to be humbled by the many ways that so many people are offering their own versions of what love, support, and kindness can be.

So many emotions have been washing over me, and I do my best to pay attention to them, one at a time, as I can touch them and feel them. The one constant is the feeling of such deep, deep gratitude. *How will I respond?* I may begin with fear, or maybe sadness, or sometimes anger, but then I will continue to respond with the one thing I can control. In any moment, I can *always* touch Gratitude.

Today I am grateful that Scott got called back to work, that I felt good enough to ride my spin bike, that I got to spend time with an old friend and a new baby, and that each day I am healing. Yes, each day I am healing.

That's all for now,
me

Wednesday, March 24, 2010 8:16 PM, EDT

Ever since I saw the first preview for the movie *Avatar*, I was intrigued and excited to see what it was all about. With all my travels and business I just couldn't seem to make it to the theater. Besides, Scott was being Scott and if he couldn't see it in IMAX 3D format . . . well, you get the idea. So when I was in Guatemala City, there was a young boy selling DVDs, and he had *Avatar* for, like, four dollars. I was pretty sure I was buying it in Spanish, but for four bucks, worst-case scenario I was helping out a local kid.

So I've had this movie for a month and no attention span to watch it, until this past Saturday. I went to my son Shaun's house, and we watched it together. I fell in love with this movie! It's as though everything I've ever believed about being beautifully connected came to life right in front of me on the screen. The use of colors, movement, fantasy, and imagery drew me in and kept me right there for the entire experience. The whole essence of "I see you" speaks to my Spirit and warms me to my bones.

My favorite scene (okay, one of my favorites) was when the lead character was officially welcomed as a member of the local clan. The ceremony began with one person laying their hand on his shoulder, and then another reached up to touch him as well. Then a chain reaction occurred, as all of the people in the village reached forward to touch the shoulder of the one in front of them. Together the entire community had formed a giant interconnected circle around this one man, completely surrounding him, allowing him to feel their strength and support. As the camera panned away, it looked like a beautiful flower.

I keep hearing that everything happens in Sacred Time and I am certain that my seeing this movie right now is perfectly, sacredly timed. I've watched it again and again and I have no doubt that my "favorite scene" is the perfect metaphor for how my cherished community of family and friends is creating the same circle around me . . . perfectly dynamic and lovingly constant.

My last post was about Gratitude, and it looks like this one is, too. The only difference is that this entire post is dedicated to each and every one of you.

You are my Lightworkers, walking buddies, crying pals, my working relief, my storytellers, book-buyers, Facebook friends, warriors and hunters. If it weren't for you, I don't think I could have gotten out of bed this morning. I see you, and I am so grateful that you see me, even when I know *this* can be hard to look at.

I love you all and I thank you for continuing to show up.

If it weren't for you, I don't think I could have gotten out of bed this morning. I see you, and I am so grateful that you see me, even when I know *this* can be hard to look at.

I love you all and I thank you for continuing to show up.

Chapter Four
How Will I Respond?

Saturday, March 27, 2010 10:52 AM, EDT

Doing it my way

This week seemed extra hard. While it was great that Scott went back to work at his concrete company, it also meant that I had a lot more time alone than I'd had alone in forever. For me, time alone means time to think . . . that is, when I'm not working. So I scheduled a lot of calls, and it was good for me to be back in touch with my teams and my docs. I managed my inbox pretty well, and all in all, I felt pretty organized.

It was the "in-betweens" that got me. I might have to create rules for me to follow about staying off the Internet. I can't imagine that it's important to do any more research on Chemo, or wigs, turbans, and scarves, or support groups. My new rule will be to start reading some of the great books that I have sitting in front of me and enjoying some of this downtime.

Back to this week: I was in a funk on Wednesday and decided I really needed to "shake up" my energy. It was extra hard to stay focused on the more positive side of things, and that's just not ever good for me. More than anything, I found myself second-guessing my ability to stay with this process. Frankly, I was feeling tired of being in the unknown, my arm was making me crazy, my chest hurt, and I was throwing a huge pity party about everything associated with Chemo. So what now? How will I respond?

When I was in my Gestalt International coaching program a couple of years ago, I met the most wonderful people. Among my new friends was a beautiful woman from Israel. Anat and I were about to work together for a coaching session, and things around us were a bit busy and scattered. I honestly don't remember who was coaching whom that time, but I do clearly remember sitting down, getting myself centered, and being very ready to begin. I asked Anat how to say "I am here" in Hebrew. She told me there were actually two ways to say it. "Ani Po" is a pretty generic way, like if you are taking roll or something. The second way is "Hineni," which has a much deeper sense of being and presence and means "fully here." That was the one I was looking for, and that word has resonated and stayed with me since.

This past week, *Hineni* began in some ways to tap me on the shoulder. My inner voice was talking to me, and I could hear it loudly saying how important it is to "be here," to stay and remain present, to really show up. This week I felt like turning to run away, but this voice, my inner voice, was reminding me about staying the course.

Now you are going to laugh, because I went back to the Internet! This time I wasn't looking up Cancer, though. I was looking up *Hineni*. Here's what I got:

> *It means, "Here I am," and is mostly used when God personally calls on someone in the Bible to do something difficult and important. Abraham? "Here I am." Moses? "Here I am." It's very complete and emotionally charged, and implies, "Here I am: ready, willing and able." There's a special prayer on Yom Kippur called "Hineni" which starts, "Here I am in deep humility . . ."*

Here I stand. It's not a meek thought; it's a bottom line. "Here I stand. Here I will make my stand. I know what will most likely happen, but it does not matter, since I will not be moving. This is where I am going to make my stand. Hineni."

Now I'm clearly not comparing little ol' me to Moses or Abraham, but whatever is happening right now, in this moment, for me, is big. Very, very big.

Here's where the story gets fun: I hear this word, this concept, this belief. How do I capture it? Hold it? Keep it? Easy—I get a tattoo! And I put it somewhere that will be right in front of me all the time as a beautiful reminder of what I know I am capable of. When I forget again, and I know I will, I want to be able to see and touch and feel it with ease. I basically broke all of my own old rules when I decided on this one. I've always believed that any tattoos I have should not be visible to the general public. But, oh well, this is my story and I can write it and live it and tell it how I want, right?

So next time you see me, ask me to show you my left wrist. Left is the side of the feminine, the side of receiving, and also the side where My Cancer found its way to my body.

    Hineni.

Saturday, March 27, 2010 12:03 PM, EDT

I know! I know! You wanted to see . . .

By the way, the sun is shining. I'm going for a walk.

Love and blessings to you,
Sheri

Wednesday, March 31, 2010 8:46 PM, EDT

Considering the experiences I've had during the past couple of weeks, I'm beginning to feel like the poster child for the Cleveland Clinic. Between surgery, oncology, and my new primary care physician, I am at my local campus at least once a week, and let me tell you, they are keeping a smile on my face.

When I'm out in the world doing what I love and earning my living (some people call it working), one of the things I am most passionate about is helping "my practices" create unique and wonderful experiences for their patients. We spend hours and hours exploring concepts like what it means to be highly engaged and fully present for each and every patient who walks through our doors. We practice skills like active listening, curiosity, and using open-ended questions so that we can develop beautiful, high-quality relationships with our patients. And then we challenge ourselves to constantly "dial up" our efforts so that our patients will continue to experience us as fresh and open to whatever new possibilities might emerge.

Oftentimes, I have found myself saying that this work we do has the potential to raise the bar on how any and all health care experiences can be. Sadly, my personal experience in health care over many decades has fallen very short of what I so passionately believe in . . . until now.

The day I met the primary surgeon who was to perform my mastectomies, he mentioned an upcoming Women's Health Symposium that he thought I might be interested in attending. He was speaking on breast issues, an OB/GYN was speaking on HPV and other screenings and such, and then there were a dozen or so tables set up with information on different Cleveland Clinic departments, boutiques for Breast Cancer patients, and so on.

My favorite part of the evening was when I saw my favorite surgeon and the surgery department team at their table. I'm almost embarrassed to tell you but I actually started to cry. I was only two weeks out of surgery, and I got the most wonderful reception from them! With great pride, I introduced them to my friend as "my surgical team," and they all got up to hug me. They knew my name and I could see and feel how much they genuinely cared. *My team*, and they care. For me, it doesn't get any better than that.

Next, my oncology team. I haven't even started my treatment, and I already feel like I have half a dozen friends ready to take care of me when I go for my infusions. When I called for my appointment, I was welcomed with open arms and invited to come tour the department the day before I was scheduled. Barb, my nurse, could hear my anxiety and wanted to ensure my comfort as early on in the process as possible.

The next day, when I left from my actual appointment, I got a phone call from the Cleveland Clinic within five minutes. Are you ready for this one? Barb called me just to say good-bye because she wasn't right there when I left! She wanted to be sure I would write down any questions as they popped up and assured me that I could call anytime for anything at all. Wow! That's what I call going the extra mile.

And lastly, my new primary care physician. When I walked in the door just two days ago to meet this woman for the very first time, her first words to me were . . . here we go . . . you're not going to believe this: "I feel as if I already know you, and I am so glad you are here." She actually read my chart before she came into the room! She knew my history! She was perfectly prepared, present, engaged, and inviting! We spent about thirty minutes together, getting to know each other, sharing stories, and talking about the things that were really important for both of us that day. I felt heard, supported, and very well cared for. And then, she asked if she could hug me. Of course, I cried some tears of gratitude, some tears of relief, and some tears just because.

I'm a little surprised at myself for devoting an entire post to my positive experiences with my local Cleveland Clinic, but hey, I am officially a raving fan, and this is my team. These are my warriors, fighting my battle, and my greatest advocates. The least I can do is publicly sing their praises. I know I couldn't be in better hands.

Tomorrow: "The Art of Growing Boobage."

> Love to all,
> Sheri

Chapter Five
The Art of Growing Boobage

Growing boobage

It's not like I woke up one day and thought, "Hmmm, I wonder what it would be like to have my breasts removed and then how in the heck we would construct new ones." Yet, Hineni, here I am, and that is exactly what is going on. I also never gave much thought to what it might feel like to have balloons placed behind the muscles in my chest and have them slowly filled. Yet, here I go with that one, too! Quite frankly, we made the first "fill" so much fun it really took almost all of the anxiety out of it. I must say that one of the things I was grateful for on Monday was that my plastic surgeon has a great sense of humor.

I wasn't sure if Scott could make the appointment, so I drove myself. My friend Kate met me there—she had agreed to be the photographer. Scott did show up, and the three of us piled into the small exam room at the plastic surgeon's office. (By the way, I am also a raving fan of his, but I can talk about him later.) Since at this point basically any and all modesty is gone on my part, I undressed and was sitting with my little sheet tied like a summer dress around me.

The expanders are empty implants that hold saline. Their purpose is to help create the space that will eventually house implants and also facilitate slowly stretching the skin, since so much had to be removed during the mastectomy process. You may remember me talking about this incredible "tightness" a few posts back. The tightness has since gotten slowly better, although I do still feel like I'm wearing a pretty tight bra pretty much all the time.

The fascinating part of these expanders is that there is a port in the upper half of them beneath the surface of the skin. The plastic surgeon finds the port by holding a magnet (yes, a magnet) over my chest, and then . . . X marks the spot. The doctor made a couple of different markings on each breast so that he would know where to put the needle. They told me this wouldn't hurt . . .

Here's how it works: a needle is placed in my port, which is connected to a giant syringe, which is tethered to a large bag holding sterile saline. The doctor inserts the needle, which I did not feel, and injects. That's all there is to it! I felt a little bit of pressure. Nothing more.

The day of surgery, he'd placed 75cc of saline into the expanders, and I've been proud of my "early puberty mounds" and happy to show almost anybody that's interested. It's funny, but emotionally, they don't feel like my breasts. They are more like any other scar, maybe on my knee or my elbow, so there isn't much of a sense of privacy (for lack of a better word). Now that he put another 50cc in the right and 25cc in the left, they are a little bigger, but I'm not yet "connected" to them as being personal or private.

Now you have to remember that these boobages have no nipples, so I'm sure that is a huge part of the emotional disconnect. I almost feel like a walking encyclopedia, helping to educate (mostly women) on what this is all about and what it means to go through this challenge.

At this point, I don't think I will need much more saline to be a comfortable size that I can live with (and not have to buy a whole new wardrobe). Scott is pretty certain that I can still use more. Men are so funny.

Anyway, other than a burning sensation for a day or two, this wasn't bad, and I will not worry about my future "fill" appointments. The next one is on Monday, and I'll let you know how it goes.

It's funny how even the language changes. I used to shop for bras with this cup or that cup size, and now my big question is, "How many cc does it take to make me just right?"

Just another day in my life. Thanks for showing up.

Love to you and look for reasons to smile today,
Sheri

Sunday, April 4, 2010 10:45 PM, EDT

Please know how much your posts mean to me and how much I enjoy knowing you have been here to visit. It doesn't matter if what you say is simple or profound, eloquent or boring. What matters is that you care. Thanks for continuing to show up, even when I may not have anything new to say.

> It doesn't matter if what you say is simple or profound, eloquent or boring. What matters is that you care.

Tuesday, April 6, 2010 2:52 PM, EDT

There are the most interesting conversations happening around me, and sometimes even with me, that go something like this: "But she just doesn't look sick."

It's true, you know. I don't *feel* sick, either. In fact, I'm even calling this point in time my "sweet spot." Surgery is four weeks behind me, my left arm is functioning at about 75 percent, I'm exercising almost every day, having no pain, and working a normal schedule. This beautiful window of feeling good is a precious gift, and I intentionally don't want to waste a moment of it. The top has been down on my orange Mini, and it's as if God is smiling and waving with the sun shining and wind blowing on these absolutely perfect days.

I don't feel sick. And yet, in fifteen days I will walk into the infusion suite of the oncology department of the Cleveland Clinic and my Chemo will begin.

Believe me, it's not like I'm planning on how sick I will be. In reality, the opposite is my truth. I am creating a clear future memory of feeling strong, with a healthy appetite and enough energy to get on my bike. I can see myself boarding an airplane to go work with my teams and staying on top of my inbox and my to-do list.

I'm also not delusional, knowing there is a strong possibility that my actual experience will be very different from the picture I've painted in my mind. It may be extremely difficult. The surgery itself was hard, but my rebound was quick and I simply didn't let it knock me down. And now, in fifteen days, it might happen that I will significantly slow down and not feel very well at all. That's why it is right now, in the sweet spot, that everything is most important.

There is not an hour that passes without my intentionally slowing down long enough to acknowledge and be thankful for any number of things. It could be the people in my life, the sun on my face, the card in the mail, or my dog cuddling up next to me. More than ever, I am so grateful for each and every conversation. Sharing stories, being in a relationship, or just "hanging out" and listening with ears that really care about what is being said has become my favorite medicine.

Last night, I found myself saying that it feels as if time has somehow slowed itself down. My sense of urgency around most things has lessened as a sense of calm has found its way into my core. Tasks are still being completed, deadlines are still being met, new ideas continue to emerge. But everything is happening more s l o w l y.

Maybe this is what it means to surrender. Maybe this is what it means to trust. Maybe this is just what happens when a person really learns way down deep about what really matters.

For today, please know that I am loving this sweet spot, and I feel a convertible ride coming as a big smile shows up on my little face.

> Love to each and every one of you,
> Sheri

Chapter Six
A Very Big Week

Saturday, April 10, 2010 6:16 PM, EDT

 Open and caring hearts

I'm warning you . . . this is a long one. This past week was among the most important for the company I represent, as our clients from all over the country came together for our annual summit. The vision for this meeting is, first and foremost, of Community, and then of Leadership and Influence. We always have it in a super-cool place, and we treat ourselves and our clients like kings and queens for a couple of days. This year's meeting was extra special for me for a couple of reasons, the first of which was simply that I felt good enough to go at all. Next, this meeting was packed full of beautiful surprises.

Let me change directions a bit. This journal has been a wonderful gift for me. It's providing a way for me to put my thoughts, experiences, and feelings into words. It's allowing anyone that cares a means of staying current with my progress. And it's also been giving each of you a way to express yourselves, tell your stories, and show me an incredible amount of love and support. This has all happened from the comfort of my own living room.

I've been able to enjoy a couple of visitors at a time, and I have been out to dinner with friends and family. All the things in this "sweet spot" have been amazing. I really did feel good enough to go to South Carolina and could feel in my bones how important it was that I attend this meeting. What I didn't expect was how different it would be from that safety of my living room.

Remember when I talked about the scene in *Avatar*, with the entire village surrounding the lead character in support as he formally joined the community? I talked about how you have all helped me feel loved and supported. I could close my eyes in any moment and feel all the love and healing energy surrounding me. I have created the perfect "virtual community"!

So one of the ways that I was surprised at this summit meeting was by how different it was to "physically" be held and surrounded by such a great number of people. Please keep in mind that I know this group. These are my friends, my clients, and my team. I feel safe and confident, and I have the highest level of trust in every person who attended. And still, I felt so exposed and so incredibly vulnerable.

So many times, I found myself in perfectly normal conversations— laughing and talking about dentistry and coaching and planning, or calling to change the temperature in the room. And then, in a split second, there would be some kind of shift, and I would be either gently or abruptly reminded that something was significantly different. I felt tightness across my chest, or someone asked me about what happens for me next. I am recovering from major surgery. I am about to start Chemo. Wow, do I feel different.

Then it would get normal again, and I would set up the projector and play a song that my boss didn't like and laugh, and find myself in a great conversation . . . and then another shift. A hug was really tight, or someone told me about their mother and Cancer. I am recovering from major surgery. I am about to start Chemo. Wow, do I feel different.

As we opened the meeting, Kirk, who is the president and CEO of our company, did the greetings. We presented the important awards for the day. When I thought he was about to introduce the keynote speaker, he started talking about me instead. In that moment, I remember starting to cry and feeling so grateful that he hadn't called me to the front of the room.

What Kirk did do was offer to the entire group special Breast Cancer pink ribbon pins that he'd had custom made. The ribbon has been tilted on its side to look like a "K" with my name on top, so it creatively reads

"Sheri K." He invited everyone to wear them in support of me. Words can't begin to describe how humbling it was to sit and take in so much care, so much love, and so much support . . . not virtually, but right there, in my total physical being.

If that in itself wasn't enough for me to absorb, when our keynote speaker began, the first thing he did was invite me to join him at the front of the room. My glasses were off, I was crying, my hands were shaking, and our guest speaker, one of the most prestigious and amazing men in our country today, asked me to pin one of these pins on his lapel. He wanted to be the first to officially wear one in support of my battle. Whew! If I had been standing naked in front of this group, I could not have felt more exposed. Yet, I was safe, I was loved, and what I was being exposed to were ginormous (yes, it's a word) open and caring hearts.

During the next two days, every person in the room was wearing one of those pins, and I was reminded with every interaction, live and in person, how generous and giving people can be to each other. I received inspiration, more gifts than I can even list, warm hugs, and more affirmations of love and continued prayers than you can imagine. And it was so hard. And it was so beautiful.

Nobody should ever have to endure losing body parts and having drugs pushed through their veins in an effort to kill an enemy as horrible as Cancer. I, of all people, did not need this experience to know how much I am loved. And still, somehow this disease has brought out the very best in the people who surround me, and they are not only willing, but they are compelled to see me through each and every step of the way, making certain that I am cared for, loved, and appreciated.

Yes, it was a very big week, for my work community . . . and for me.

Blessings,
Sheri

Monday, April 12, 2010 8:07 PM, EDT

I have a couple of different pieces of homework from my health care providers. The general surgeon has me doing range-of-motion exercises in an effort to regain as much use of my left arm as possible. My dietitian has me drinking two smoothies a day to get all the necessary antioxidants and protein for strength and healing. And my plastic surgeon feels very strongly about having me massage the incision areas to keep scar tissue down and also massage where the expanders are to keep them pliable.

I am proud to say that I have been following most orders pretty well and doing what I can to promote healing and build my immune system. I've been exercising most days, watching what I eat, and getting good rest. I've also been doing the diligence and massaging "every hour on the hour" whenever I am home.

Anyway, when I left the plastic surgeon's office last week after having more saline injected, it was a beautiful day. I put the top down on my orange Mini and was looking forward to shopping for new clothes for a meeting in South Carolina. I drove away and stopped at a red light.

Quite mindlessly I found myself following directions, massaging my now fuller expanders and honestly feeling pretty good about my newly blossoming boobage. At that very same moment, I looked up to the right and realized that the guy in the truck next to me was getting quite the eyeful, and he had the strangest look on his face that I had ever seen! Holy crap! The light couldn't change fast enough, and I've never been happier to shift into first gear and start rolling!

Some days all I can do is laugh out loud at how outrageous this whole thing is. I hope you are smiling, too. And no, I don't have a picture.

Now, I also want to provide a strategic update.

Friday, I am having a surgical procedure performed to have a central line and port placed that they will use to infuse the Chemo.

Chemo begins next Thursday, April 22.

I will have Chemo every two weeks for sixteen weeks.

If we keep to the schedule, I will be done with Chemo on July 29.

Hineni.

Then we celebrate!

> Love to you, and I'll "talk" to you soon,
> Sheri

Friday, April 16, 2010 9:11 PM, EDT

As soon as I got on the plane last night to come home from working out of state, the woman next to me struck up a conversation. Believe it or not, I don't usually talk much on planes, especially after a big visit with a team. Yes, even Sheri Kay gets tired at least once in a while, and I really enjoy either reading, sleeping, or watching a movie.

It was a great conversation, though. Her work is fascinating, her energy lively, and we enjoyed comparing notes on being "women on the road." As one thing led to another, I began to share my story. She had a lot of questions and, me being me, I enjoyed answering them. We both were nicely engaged.

At one point, she got a very serious look on her face and told me that she really "admired my positive attitude" and asked me how I "did it." Without even thinking I found myself responding that "every minute is a choice." (Sometimes I can surprise even me with what comes out of my mouth.) Every minute is a choice. I also know that, inside my own humanness, some of the minutes and some of the choosing is hard.

When I landed in Ohio it was about 7:30 last night, temperature about 80 degrees, and a perfect evening for a ride with the top down on my Mini. (Please know that I kept both hands on the steering wheel to make sure that no truckers would be telling any stories about me.) I enmeshed myself in what I call "convertible therapy," because I could also feel my anxiety beginning to rise.

The past three days were all about my work and all about focusing my attention on helping other people learn and grow. Now that I'd landed back home, my intention needed to shift. I had to be at the hospital at 6:30 the next morning for a surgical procedure to have my port placed. I was getting scared. Please understand that my fear had nothing at all to do with the actual surgery and everything to do with what it stood for. I was about to take that first *giant* step toward Chemo.

Fifteen minutes after I walked in the door, Scott was busy working on a door frame because Scott is always busy doing something (I love him), and like an ocean wave it came rushing over me. My whole body started to shake and my tears began to flow. I asked Scott to please stop what he was doing for just a moment . . .

It seemed like a really long time but it was probably only a minute or two that he did exactly what I needed him to do. Scottie held me and let me cry, and cry, and cry. I looked up and all I could say was, *"I don't want to do this! I don't want a port! I don't want Chemo! I just want to work and travel and ride my bike!"*

Scott didn't have to say a word. He kept me wrapped in his arms, standing in the kitchen, until I calmed myself down. My focus was now on my breathing and slowing down my heart rate.

> Some minutes are about fear and some about anger and some are so full of being so very sad. Sometimes it's hard for me to remember that those minutes are every bit as important as the minutes of strength and gratitude.

Cory (my younger son) had come in the house at this point and he was very present for me. I was grateful for his hugs, too, and then he went out to our patio and got a fire going. Scott went back to his project, and Cory and I worked to build and nurture and coax a fire to life in the pit. I had the gift of more minutes. Minutes to talk, minutes to cry again, minutes to laugh, and minutes to relax and simply enjoy the fire. Every minute I got to make a new choice.

Thanks to all of you for reminding me that it's okay, and for nurturing me through the minutes when I am not full of smiles and not full of hope. Some minutes are about fear and some about anger and some are so full of being so very sad. Sometimes it's hard for me to remember that those minutes are every bit as important as the minutes of strength and gratitude.

In the end, my procedure went really well today. I love my surgeon and had another great experience with the surgical team at the Cleveland Clinic. My mom was able to be with me at the Clinic, and I enjoyed having her over for a few hours, taking great care of me. Rumor has it that I'm quite entertaining when I'm on pain meds, and I know she likes being able to hang out and "be Mom."

So this giant step has been taken. The port is in place, and I'm now six days away from my first Chemo. I'm not sure how many minutes that is, but I will keep reminding myself over and over that each minute truly does come with a choice.

Please know that, for me, this minute is a good one.

       Sheri

Chapter Seven
The Cell Phone Rings

Monday, April 19, 2010 11:58 AM, EDT

Today my head is filled with tons and tons of questions, and as usual, with more metaphors than I can track in any given moment. I'm honestly not sure when I began to find the poetry in almost everything. My best guess is that I've always experienced a lot in my head, and now I've found a way to put language to all that internal noise.

A few weeks ago, my brother told me about a Cleveland Orchestra concert that he thought I would enjoy. Knowing that my port surgery was on Friday, I was pretty confident that by Sunday I would feel good enough to go. We ordered a block of tickets for my family, and yesterday we excitedly made our way down to the first and second rows of the hall.

The guest conductor was a pianist who led the orchestra through some of the most beautiful music my ears have ever heard. Her use of her entire body from the piano bench took my breath away over and over again—it was if she were creating an invitational dance for the musicians to join. And they did. The violinist who was just over her right shoulder was in the musical dance with her, anticipating every note and engaged in her every move.

I'm certain that much of my experience was heightened by the close proximity I had to the orchestra. It was as though I was right there with each of them inside of the music and feeling it in my own body. I must admit that I felt physically tired, just coming off the pain medication, and my body still wanting rest. Yet, I was being infused with this incredible energy that was filling my Spirit and lifting my soul. It was a beautiful, magical feeling.

After the intermission and during the final concerto it happened . . . vaguely at first, since the music was alive, and then it got louder as the music was coming to a natural pause . . . *a cell phone was ringing somewhere in the crowd.*

I can't begin to help you understand what it felt like in the music hall. I could feel myself gasp and I thanked the Lord that it wasn't my phone. My anxiety went really high. I saw the violinist completely change his expression to what I interpreted as disgust, the piano *stopped*, and the orchestra fell silent. I'm not sure why, but I was embarrassed—I guess because I was part of this crowd, part of this community, and one of us had failed miserably in being respectful toward the matriarch in the room.

She paused for a very, very, very long ten or fifteen seconds. She raised her arms, held them there for a moment, then perfectly and wonderfully brought the music back to life. I was in awe of her ability to get present and to re-engage so quickly after having such a huge negative shift in the energy.

I don't know that I ever was able to fully re-engage myself. I was distracted and found my mind wandering to hundreds of places. More than anything, I was so deeply curious about how that event had impacted the conductor and each of the different musicians. Were they all knocked off balance? How was it that they could all re-enter after such a shift? Does this happen often? Were we a bad audience because one person in the crowd screwed up?

This session was being recorded. Was it ruined? Could they fix it? I felt so bad. I wanted to let it go and pay attention. I didn't want to waste a moment of the beauty of the music, so how could I shift back? Would it ever be the same? Can I remember this concert without also remembering the cell phone ringing?

Ahh . . . the metaphors.

Here I am every day, showing up for my life. *Playing my music* the only way I know—by coaching, by loving, and even by riding my bike. Then *the cell phone rings.* For me, it is Breast Cancer. Funny, all the questions still apply. What do any of us do when the "cell phone rings"?

It truly was a wonderful and amazing concert. Just for the record, there were at least 247 other metaphors that I experienced other than those involving the cell phone.

Thanks for the day, Big Brother. I loved all of it.

Tuesday, April 20, 2010 8:30 PM, EDT

All I can say is . . . "what a day."

Part of me thought about waiting until I know for sure what will happen before I made an entry in this journal. The rest of me decided to invite all of you to ride this roller coaster right along with me. After all, what are friends for?

It was supposed to be a pretty good day. A quick and easy appointment to my favorite plastic surgeon to grow a little more boobage was to be first thing in the morning. I had asked a friend of mine to join me for the saline fill-up and knew we would have a great conversation and laugh a lot on the drive back and forth. I was then going to make a bunch of coaching calls and work on a strategy to once again catch up on my emails. Great plan, right? (I remember, a long time ago, somebody told me that *plans make God laugh*.)

Jill picked me up at 8:30, and off we went. We did have a great conversation and arrived at the office in perfect time. Off comes the shirt, on comes the sexy sheet, and the treatment coordinator begins to prepare my injection. I asked her to check a small area along my left incision that had "oozed" a little in the past few days. I was not really concerned, just aware that a small area (half the size of a pencil eraser) looked a little red. In my own mind I figured they might decide not to fill me up as much as we had talked about.

Nope. I was way wrong. The doctor was very concerned—so concerned that he talked about doing a surgical procedure today. I heard something about infection, something else about concern that the expander might be compromised, and something else about postponing Chemo. I must have gone pale, because I then heard Jill saying to me that everything would be fine.

47

Within ten minutes of entering the office, we were back on our way toward my house with instructions to be at the local hospital at 4:30 that afternoon for a procedure to repair the dehiscence, which is a problem with the way the tissues along the sutures were healing. I was assured that this was a short and simple process, with the risk of either finding damage from an infection or possibly creating damage to my expander while doing what we needed to do to fix the tissue.

The worst part was facing the possibility that my first Chemo might have to be delayed. Have you said, "Oh, shit," yet? Talk about a "cell phone ringing," an interruption, a glitch in the matrix. This whole thing is bad enough without adding even more stress, another procedure, and a change in my Chemo plan that I am perfectly emotionally, physically, and mentally prepared for.

I literally had to keep reminding myself to breathe.

When I got home and stared at my schedule, I gave good thought to cancelling all calls and sitting on the couch all day, watching movies and crying. Instead, I made a few calls to friends to first let myself cry and then get myself calmed down. I made the decision to distract myself with work, and settled in with my laptop and my phone.

Sitting here and freaking out was not going to do me any good. Sitting here and being present to other people and talking about what I know could give me some control back . . . I liked this. And it worked. In fact, I was pretty damn creative today, if I do say so myself.

During the in-betweens was a little challenging.

I just don't feel like having another surgery. I just HAD surgery on Friday. I don't want to delay Chemo. I'm ready for my Chemo NOW.

I feel like going on a cruise.

If they delay Chemo, maybe I can sneak in a business trip. My whole schedule will be off. This sucks.

I know, I'll make a smoothie . . .

I called Scott to make sure he could come right home after work, and by 4 p.m. we were on our way to the hospital. It was about 5:30 before the surgeon came in, and by 5:45 I was wheeled into the OR.

It's actually a pretty cool experience to be 100 percent awake during a surgical procedure. Honestly, it was all I could do to stay quiet and not ask a million questions. It was all I could do to not jump off the table and want to help. I did ask them where the mirror was so I could watch. Instead, they covered my face with a blue thing.

I was most grateful for the conversations among the small surgical team as they did their dance of getting ready and actually doing the procedure. They were great about telling me what was happening and what I would feel and why. "Cold rinse here, warm towel there," and that sort of thing. My assumption is that the majority of people they treat in the OR are very asleep, so having them involve me and include me was not only thoughtful, it helped me manage my anxiety and stay calm. Start to finish, it took maybe fifteen minutes.

The tissue will be cultured to see if there is an infection, and I'm now on antibiotics. The expander stayed intact, and the underlying tissue and the tissue matrix "look great." The doctor's best guess is that this small area simply did not have adequate blood supply to remain vital and heal itself. The incision was very close to a previous scar from my first biopsy three years ago, so that tissue had already been compromised.

My surgeon is pretty sure that Chemo should wait a week. Chemo attacks dividing cells, including cells involved in the healing process— and we need this surgical site to heal. The ultimate decision will lie in the hands of my oncologist, and he will be involved tomorrow.

Emotionally, I really want to begin treatment on Thursday. Intellectually, it seems to make sense to wait. I'm actually happy that it's not up to me. My brain is too full of worry about making the wrong decision. Sometime tomorrow, we will all know, and now that I made it through the day, whatever they decide is okay by me.

After all, it's just another part of the story, right?

Okay, what was one thing that put a smile on my face today? One of the surgical techs gave me a smile and thanked me for being such a good patient. In the context of a very scary and anxious day, it felt so good to get such a beautiful compliment from one of my care providers.

One of the surgical techs gave me a smile and thanked me for being such a good patient. In the context of a very scary and anxious day, it felt so good to get such a beautiful compliment from one of my care providers.

To all my clients and team members out there: take the previous paragraph to heart. His words made all the difference for me today.

I'm breathing now.

Sheri

Wednesday, April 21, 2010 8:59 PM, EDT

Quick update: decision was made to wait one week before I start my Chemo. One week from yesterday, that is. So I am not beginning Chemo tomorrow. My start day is now Tuesday.

I left the emotional roller coaster from yesterday in yesterday and was happy to wake up this morning to a new day.

A dear friend of mine flew in from Arizona to be with me for the first round. I guess we'll be thinking of something way more fun to do over the next few days!

All is well and I'll use this time to rest and play and move around my schedule for next week.

Love and hugs,
Sheri

Sunday, April 25, 2010 9:33 AM, EDT

It's a pleasure to wake up with the sun shining and anticipation of a beautiful day. Although it is supposed to rain much later, I think Scott and I will be able to get out for a bike ride. Twenty miles sounds really good today.

It was just a week ago on Friday that I had my port placed, and although I'm not in any pain, it still feels very odd to have a foreign body placed under my skin in the upper corner of my front. And it's pretty big, so when I reach forward or reach my arm across, I can feel it there. Again, it doesn't hurt, but I'm not sure how it will feel to reach out to my bicycle handlebars. We will find out soon!

In some ways, today and tomorrow are like slowly "walking the plank." I was counting the days to Chemo before and then had this interruption. So here I go again, knowing, and not knowing at all, what to expect on Tuesday. So today and tomorrow could be just a little predictable. I can have some plans. I know how I feel and what I'm capable and not capable of . . . to some extent, anyway.

I did have a great time with my friend, Jane R., being here. She got to visit with some folks she had not seen in ten or more years, and we got some creative work started. It was really fun to bring out my sewing machine and learn a tiny, tiny bit about quilting. She is a master quilter and got me started on a project I've been wanting to do for a long time. She also helped me learn how to make my own head scarves, which I will be needing pretty soon, when my hair starts to go.

I told Jane that, in a way, making my own scarves feels a bit like digging my own grave. It's hard knowing that something so emotionally challenging is about to happen. Yet, there is that wonderful feeling of control when I get to participate fashionably in the "how" of it all.

It was like that on the day when I went to pick out my wig. I obviously don't like that my hair will fall out, but I do get to make some decisions about what I will put on my head when it happens. I won't be able to pick the day when it starts to fall out, but I can choose to cut it early, and I can grab the clippers and take ownership of the process once it starts.

When I can participate, rather than have things just happen, I can manage pretty well. It's the days with the surprises that I don't like so much. Ya know?

I clearly remember one of my faculty from Gestalt saying, "Whenever something happens that is different from what we expect, we often experience that as personal failure." It takes great intention to reframe these "different experiences" into something other than failure, at least for me. Herein lies my work. This is where I have so much room for learning and (whether I always like it or not) opportunity for growth.

I also want to acknowledge and truly honor the amazing and special and wonderful surprises. These have become my sanity, my saving grace, and my inspiration. The little special surprises give me strength and a good reason to get up every morning to face the day.

Yesterday, I received an extra bunch of cards in the mail and realized that there has not been a single day when at least one card did not show up in the mail for me. I love my cards and keep and reread them often. It's crazy fun to read them over, especially since many came when I was medicated. I feel like I'm getting them for the first time all over!

Just for the record, part of my brain clearly fell out when I got my diagnosis, because I am forgetting a lot of things. Please be understanding if we have a conversation and I don't remember something. I'm simply accepting this as part of my current reality.

In the mail yesterday was a CD from my brother. My goosebumps were on top of my goosebumps when I opened it! Mitsuko Uchida! This CD is by the pianist/conductor we heard last Sunday. The CD includes the same piece of music that was "interrupted" with the cell phone, only this time she is performing with the English Chamber Orchestra, and I love it. This music will be on my Most Played list in the months to come, as it has such a beautiful, calming yet lively energy for me. Thanks, Big Brother.

Another surprise that makes me smile comes from all my friends near and far who are finding and connecting in person, on Facebook, through this online journal, on the phone, and through every other form of media available. I feel like a giant magnet and love that I am attracting so many great people into and back into my life.

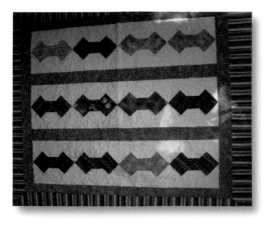

A gift from Jane

In this picture you see the most beautiful quilt ever. This was my surprise from Jane. Remember I told you she is a master quilter? She remembered that when her brother had Chemo he was cold all the time, so she found this pattern on a Breast Cancer something-or-other site and put this together for me! See?

Some surprises are perfect and fun and full of joy. Some surprises are worth getting up for.

I love the little surprise visits, the calls, the posts, the emails, and the "stuff for the basket." (What is that, anyway? When will I find out?) Please know how much I appreciate your time, and thank you for being in this for the long haul. My biggest surprise is that here we are, two months into this, and I still am not alone. You are still here. We are in this together.

> Two days to go.
> Bike ride today.
> Work tomorrow.
> Chemo on Tuesday.

I hope any surprises you have today make you smile.

> 'Bye for now,
> Sheri

Chapter Eight
Seven More Times to Get It Right

Monday, April 26, 2010 8:14 PM, EDT

Traveling for work over 100 days a year, I certainly have a good amount of experience packing. I typically check the weather, think about what I want to wear, and then gather all necessary supplies. It's a breeze. In fact, I can do it running fully on automatic while putting away laundry and talking on the phone.

Now here I am, staring at everything I own, and I don't have a clue at all about how to pack. After all, how does one know how to pack for the first day of Chemo? I don't know what the office temperature is like. I know I want to be wearing something comfortable, but I need to make sure they can get to my port. Can I wear a pretty shirt, or will I maybe bleed when they hook me up? Will I be tired and restful, or do I want to take a bunch of things to keep me busy? Where is my iPod and do I need to charge it?

Little by little, though, I am realizing that things seem to have somehow organized themselves around me.

Today a friend of mine stopped over with a big *orange* canvas bag with all kinds of goodies inside that she thought would be good for me to take along. I added my new favorite book, *Spot of Grace* by Dawna Markova, given to me by another friend, and grabbed my new Chemo quilt made by Jane.

This is good. I'm starting a pile.

Next, for the past couple of weeks I've been getting envelopes and small packages from all over the country marked "for the basket" on the outside. I had gotten instructions from Rachael to put them away *unopened* until I got to Chemo. The rest of my instructions were to take a few at a time to each treatment, and there "should be enough to have some for all eight treatments." When I told my sister about this today, she said it was like Chanukah! Yep! Eight days of presents, eight days of surprises.

It's really fun for me to follow rules—*yeah, right*—but this time I am actually doing it. I just grabbed a handful of cards and added them to the growing heap on the couch. I can't wait to see what this is all about, and I promise to fill you in on details as they unfold. I don't know what the basket is, but I do already know that this is another huge way that my special caring circle is showing up to make sure I'm OK.

Right on the coffee table in front of me is the CD from my brother. Since I hadn't yet uploaded the music to my iPod, that is happening right now. I can feel myself relax and I'm remembering to breathe.

Clothes are figured out. Yoga pants, orange tank top, and very comfy sweater. No sandals. My feet might get cold. Hmmm, this isn't bad at all. See? It all got organized around me.

The big questions that everyone is asking:

Are you ready?

Funny thing: I thought I was ready last week and I don't even know what that means. I've done everything I could think of to prepare physically, emotionally, and spiritually.

I began acupuncture to help reduce my anxiety and also help support my "about to be compromised" immune system. I saw the acupuncturist today and also had a great chiropractic adjustment. We did some creative light and Chakra work and I left feeling pretty balanced.

Today I also went to have my near-perfect and very beautiful acrylic nails removed. I never understood why people would waste money on such a time-consuming and relatively expensive thing. And then I started getting mine done. It was worth every penny to have awesome-looking nails every day without my ever touching them, and also to have an excuse to take an hour just for me every three or four weeks.

In preparation for Chemo, it was suggested that I have the acrylic nails removed. Although they could be fine, there are many risks for someone with a poor immune system. So, I'm doing what I can to minimize as many of those risks as possible. It wasn't traumatic or anything, but it was sad (and not very comfortable). When I look down and see my poor thin and not-so-pretty nails, I'll just have to turn my hand over and meditate on my tattoo.

My favorite part of the day came when our friends Dave and Guilda came by to offer a beautiful blessing to both Scott and me. We did a meditation along with a sweet little ceremony, and they snuck away as I dozed off for a short nap. I do have the coolest friends.

Who's taking me?

My mom, of course! Scott is back to work at the concrete company, and unless he gets rained out, it will be just us. Mom wouldn't miss being there for anything, regardless of who else might be there. It's an understatement to say that I've been worried about my parents in this entire Cancer scene. This is hard, and nothing is harder than watching your kid go through something like this. I get that. I'm also more grateful than words can express to have my mom by my side each and every step of this adventure. (Stop crying, Mom. I just wanted to say thanks and I love you. But I know you already know that.)

I'm also more grateful than words can express to have my mom by my side each and every step of this adventure.

As I look over at my loveseat, it appears that everything is ready. If I forgot something, oh well. There are, after all, seven more times to get it right.

> Love to you all,
> Sheri

Chapter Nine
In Like A Lamb, Out Like A Lion

Tuesday, April 27, 2010 1:59 PM, EDT

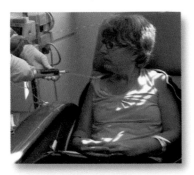

The color for today is RED 'cause that was the color of my first liquid warrior medicine. The other one was clear, and I don't think that would make for a very good entry.

All in all, today went well. Not too much anxiety going in. Mom and Scott were both there. Dad, Shaun, and my cantor all came by for short visits, and start to finish was about four hours.

It did hurt for a quick second when they accessed the port (put the needle in), but then we pretty much just hung out. I opened some of my wonderful cards that were reserved for today, and I thank whoever thought of this beautiful idea. Reading and playing with what was inside quickly became both a perfect diversion and an easy way to get centered in my process.

There were some interesting sensations, like a funny taste in my mouth here and there, some pressure in and around my eyes, and I couldn't decide if I was warm or cool. The quilt was perfect, and I was able to settle in and take a short nap listening to my new favorite pianist.

I'll end by letting you know that other than being tired and looking a bit pale, I feel downright normal. My moment of laughter? Seems my

Chemo has the ability to turn my pee a different color. Any guesses? Yep. It's *orange*. I think this is flippin' hysterical.

One down. Seven to go.

Here's to great meds and no nausea in the days to come!

Much love,
Sheri

Wednesday, April 28, 2010 7:48 AM, EDT

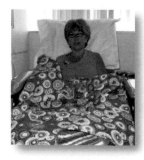

The infusion
wasn't so bad . . .

Well, friends, if yesterday morning came in like a lamb, it certainly went out like a lion.

Thankfully, I was able to rest throughout the day. I enjoyed music, some TV, a couple of naps, and even a really nice coaching call at the end of the day. I was also acutely aware of very subtle changes with my body all day long. I was warm and chilled, pretty "tingly" all over in spurts (no fever), with an unwelcome growing state of heartburn coupled with low-level nausea.

By evening time I had significant belly cramps, and just after 9 o'clock . . . I blew. The most upsetting part for me was that I got sick just ten minutes after I had taken my sleeping pill. Gone. More than anything, I really wanted to sleep. Fortunately, getting sick left me feeling 90 percent better, a welcome relief from both the heartburn and the nausea. I won't say last night was the best night's sleep I ever had, but I did sleep.

I know I've talked before about things like "control" and "interruptions." I also know that nobody can go through every minute or hour or day wondering and worrying about what will happen next. We'd all be in a constant state of anxiety and it would be virtually impossible to enjoy life.

Yet on a day like yesterday, when I was in such a high state of awareness with my own body, I got an even deeper glimpse into what it means to fully surrender. I had geared myself up and psyched myself out to believe that I would feel nothing but good yesterday. I'd planned on napping, watching a movie, and enjoying the evening. I was NOT going to get sick, and I had heavy-duty IV antiemetics on board to help ensure that everything went according to plan. Damn plans.

> I got sick and I got over it. I know it could have been a lot worse, and it wasn't. Lots of things happen that we don't want to happen, right? We dump it in the toilet and move on to what's next. That's what I'm doing, anyway.

But, oh well. I got sick and I got over it. I know it could have been a lot worse, and it wasn't. Lots of things happen that we don't want to happen, right? We dump it in the toilet and move on to what's next. That's what I'm doing, anyway.

Today, I go back for a quick injection. I will always get this 24 hours after my Chemo to begin restoration of my immune system. They said it could cause "bone pain." That just doesn't sound good at all . . . but I will hope for the best and let you know what I experience with this one.

Your cards, calls, and posts continue to inspire and enlighten me. Thank you. Thank you.

Oh, and I woke up and pulled on my hair. It's still there! It probably won't do anything for a couple of weeks, but I just couldn't help myself.

> Hugs and smiles,
> Sheri

It seems like twenty years since I wrote anything here, although I have made dozens of entries in my mind. Here it is, Saturday morning, and I am cautiously confident that I am officially on the "other side" of feeling like crap.

I do think that Thursday was the worst day in terms of body aches, but yesterday I just couldn't seem to wake up. So me, my couch, and my dog had quite a nice day of rest. I was struggling with a headache that I'm sure came from not eating . . . quite a little cycle. But no appetite is *really* no appetite.

On one hand, it feels and sounds horrible to know that this will be my cycle for seven more treatments. On the other hand, here it is Saturday, I think the worst is behind me, and I can gear up to feel good until we do this again. The best part of that last statement is my ability to use the word "we."

The "we" is everything to me. It's been interesting the past few days, because I could literally feel the sense of "pause" coming from my virtual community. The phone slowed a bit, the visits calmed, the emails quieted . . . all in response to me beginning my Chemo. Please hear me: it has been the perfect pause. I can still feel you with me, hear your voices, and sense your presence. Nobody left, and I had the space that I didn't even know I needed.

By the way, I continue to tug on my hair, and at least for now it is staying put. Oh, the simple pleasures . . .

> Love 2 u today,
> Sheri

Maybe it's because I travel a lot that every once in a while I find that I'm crazy overcommitted, and I'm just not quite sure how I have so much that I really have to get done. I start to touch that feeling of being overwhelmed, my anxiety goes up just a bit, and I know that it will be helpful to shift my thinking if I want to get through it well. That has become my goal. I don't merely want to get through whatever "it" is. I want to get through it "well."

Looking back at who I was when I was a kid, this entire conversation is pretty hilarious. In my early days, all I wanted was to find the fastest, easiest path to anywhere, and I was downright devoted to cutting corners and doing the least possible of anything to make something happen.

When my boys were little, something big changed. Way down deep inside me, I realized that I wanted something different, and I knew that it would take big planning and hard work to make "it" happen.

And so it began: *long-term vision and short-term goals.*

What I wanted was too big and too far away, so I needed to make it doable. I needed to make it attainable. I started to learn to plan, to create a guideline, a structure to follow, a path. I could do one step at a time. Even looking back, I remember that when I got too far ahead of myself, I would panic and question myself. I learned then the power in asking for support, developing study groups, and surrounding myself with other people who shared a similar vision. *Long-term vision and short-term goals.*

When Scott bought me my first adult bike, I honestly didn't think I could ever ride more than a couple of miles. In my head, I was still the little kid who'd passed out on my bike in 1971. I remember the year, because the *Roger Blough* caught fire in the Lorain shipyard the same day. I don't think I had ridden since. I didn't think I could do it.

Scott got me going one mile at a time. I cried the first time I rode 25 whole miles in one day! We did it in Columbus at an organized ride in the zoo, and I was so excited! Then we did 40, then 50, and in 1993, I rode in my first "MS 150" (and yes, I was on a single bike). I biked 150 miles in two days to raise money for the National MS Society. I cried the last few miles, so incredibly tired and proud that I had done something I never imagined I could do.

Now here I am in the midst of my Chemo, and last night I decided that I'm not having fun and this is more than I feel like doing. It took me about half a second and I was able to screw my head back on straight. I know this feeling of being overwhelmed, of being overcommitted, of having more in front of me than I want to handle. I know what I need: *long-term vision and short-term goals.*

So here's my new plan. It may sound like the same plan to you, but it feels very different in my own head. Seven treatments are too many . . . too big, too much. Since I have two different cocktails of four treatments each, I've decided that I am now about to do the second of two treatments in a series of four. That will make me halfway done with the first segment next week. All I have to do is finish the first four and then I can face the next four. See, doesn't that feel just a little bit easier? I can feel myself breathe better, relax a little, and settle into this with a bit more grace.

Long-term vision and short-term goals.

And so it is . . .
Sheri

> I know this feeling of being overwhelmed, of being overcommitted, of having more in front of me than I want to handle. I know what I need: long-term vision and short-term goals.

Thursday, May 6, 2010 9:12 AM, EDT

It is so fun to tell you that I woke up feeling so sore today and I couldn't be happier. My workout yesterday was the best I've had in weeks, and I could hardly squat on the toilet this morning without "feeling the burn" in my legs. Yay!

On one hand, I fear sounding incredibly cliché. On the other hand, this intense feeling of gratitude and awareness of what is possible in every single day is very real.

Working out is such a simple thing to do right here in my own house. Yet on most days, it would take more mental effort than I care to admit to make me get up and get to it. And if I'm going to be all honest and everything, I didn't always win the argument with myself, so more days than not I wouldn't work out.

And then last week happened. Chemo kicked my little ass for a few days, and I became fully aware of just how much I wanted to be moving. My muscles wanted to be challenged and my body needed activity. A little voice in my head was yelling at me that my body wanted to fight to be healthy. My body, however, was fighting back and yelling at the top of its lungs, "Rest!" And rest I did . . . until my body let me know that it was ready for more.

Now, don't get all crazy on me, making up pictures of me running a marathon or lifting incredible weights. What I did this week has been moderate and perfectly plenty for what my body is ready for. I've been on my spin bike three days in a row, done some light lifting, started to learn how to use our new equipment in the orange room, and enjoyed doing what I know how to do on my fitness ball. But here's the thing: I didn't have to argue with me to do any of it.

It feels so good to wake up with energy and start my day with movement. Actually, it's even smaller than that. It feels good to wake up and be able to really start my day. I'm enjoying my pace and how I'm organizing my days. Visiting friends, working on my sewing project (I haven't had a sewing project in decades!), making my work calls, and riding in the convertible are all so wonderfully filling my days.

For the first time in a long time, I don't feel like any of my minutes are being wasted, because almost all the time when I pause and pay attention I can feel me smiling. It's fun to be so full of choice in how I'm spending my minutes, because each and every one of them when I'm feeling good is a gift.

I caught Melissa Etheridge on a television talk show for just a few minutes yesterday and she was talking about her own experience with Cancer. What I heard her say was that Cancer was a gift because it helped her look at life differently and become more appreciative. Yes, it does sound cliché, but it's also still true. She also said that nobody should wait for Cancer to come knocking on their door before realizing what their life can be. Yes, it does sound cliché, but it's also still true.

Maybe today will sound like one big cliché, and to be honest I don't care. Because for me, life is good this week, and that is very true.

> For the first time in a long time, I don't feel like any of my minutes are being wasted, because almost all the time when I pause and pay attention I can feel me smiling. It's fun to be so full of choice in how I'm spending my minutes, because each and every one of them when I'm feeling good is a gift.

All week I've been looking forward to tomorrow, because I get to visit my favorite plastic surgeon. You remember that my last boobage fill-up was postponed and I had a small surgery instead. I'm proud to tell you that I'm perfectly healed and ready to see what I'll look like with another 75cc or so of blossoming chest. The list of things that I am enjoying about this entire Cancer thing is pretty short. So please smile with me as I take this one little thing and make a big deal out of it. I think it's pretty flippin' cool that they can grow these things right before our very eyes.

I'm still tugging on my hair. Here we are, just over one week since my first Chemo, and it's still here. Yesterday, I did experience a lot of tingling and even a heat-like "skin-crawly" feeling all over and especially on my head. I'm not sure if that means anything at all, but each day I find myself more surprised that it's not starting to go. They said two weeks or more. Maybe this is me just being competitive or simply wanting the tension of waiting to be over. I know I could go ahead and just do the buzz, but I have to admit I'm curious about how this whole thing will play itself out.

Looking outside, I see the sun shining and I'm looking forward to a great day! Hope you are doing the same.

Love to you,
Sheri

Chapter Ten
I Am Still Me

First and most important, Happy Mother's Day to all the special women out there. Every day there has to be something to celebrate, and today is about the mother in everyone, every bit of nurturing and loving hands and hearts that keep the world going. I know that gratitude has been a golden thread weaving through all of my journal entries, and today is no different. I am especially grateful for my God-given mother. I'm also very grateful for all the amazing women in my life who have helped me grow and become the woman I am today. It's an awakening experience to take a few minutes to reflect on just how many women have shown up as "mother" during different times in my life and how I was gifted with so much diversity in terms of what that care looked like.

I also find myself smiling as I think about all of my boys' friends who have become part of our family over the years. Nothing makes me smile more than when these "grown men" wrap me in their arms and say "Hi, Momma." I think of my students and my young mentees throughout the country that I have had the pleasure of "mothering" myself. Although we typically don't have much idea how we actually influence others, I do know that each moment we are breathing, we are influencing.

I revel in taking responsibility for that awareness and commit to being both thoughtful and intentional about how I may influence anyone I connect with throughout each day. Now that I've said that out loud, it feels way bigger than "mother" and absolutely about simply being a good person. The question is not *if* we will influence, the question is *how* we will influence.

With this past week being such a really great week, I've been thinking a lot about how that happened. Two things especially shaped my week.

Monday evening, two of my girlfriends showed up for a planned visit. Well, one was planned and the other was a surprise.

We had talked about doing some body work, so it was a bonus to find myself on the massage table in the orange room having them both channel energy to me. We played beautiful, calming music and they each worked their magic. Through a very gentle, loving touch I experienced both cranial-sacral work and another Eastern modality (sorry, can't remember what it's called) that took me to a deep and peaceful place of surrender and meditation.

For me, the act of giving comes as naturally as breathing. It's so easy to do, to offer, to donate, to express. It's the act of receiving that is so very hard. This entire Cancer experience is a huge teacher for me, and learning to receive is probably the hardest lesson of all, especially when what I am receiving is so disproportionate to what I am able to give back. And yet, I am the diligent student. I am allowing myself to receive, in more ways than I ever imagined.

> This entire Cancer experience is a huge teacher for me, and learning to receive is probably the hardest lesson of all, especially when what I am receiving is so disproportionate to what I am able to give back.

During this body work session, it was as though I melted into the table, allowing myself to fully experience the healing that was being so generously offered. I do think that healing is something we have to accept in order to have it occur. It is no easy task for me to fully relax. It is no easy task for me to fully accept. It is no easy task for me to allow myself to spiritually heal from the attack on my little physical body. And yet . . . I am learning the lesson. I am asking for, inviting, accepting, and welcoming in gratitude all that is being offered.

The second big thing happened when I went for a massage. I was afraid I would scare the poor therapist with all my foreign body issues. Let's see: double mastectomies with internal expanders that extend all along the side of my body, a Chemo port that looks a little like a baby alien living in my chest, and a good possibility that I wouldn't be able to lie on my belly. If I were about to work on someone I'd never met with all this happening, I might get a little freaked out, but . . .

The therapist was amazing. Although I typically love a very deep tissue massage, she was able to get to every spot that needed attention in a gentle, firm, sensitive, and confident way that I never could have imagined. If something wasn't comfortable or if I couldn't lie one way, she would gently help me get more comfortable, and she still was able to continue and patiently work with me. She spent a long time with me before and also after to make sure I was okay, and we talked about continuing to work together throughout the remaining course of my treatment.

My big lesson for the week was about how much the act of being touched is helping to heal my Spirit. I am 100 percent sure that it is also helping to heal my body. Human touch: it's what we were designed for.

> connection . . .
> loving energy . . .
> intention . . .
> sharing . . .
> influence . . .
> healing . . .

I am so grateful, as always, to all of you, and I will continue to humbly accept all that you are giving me on this Mother's Day and every day.

Still tugging on my hair—only today, it is actually starting to come out. Lots in the shower, so I'm thinking there may be a ceremony at my house very soon. Looks like a new layer of reality is about to unveil itself.

> Blessings,
> Sheri

If there is strength in numbers, then being surrounded by people I care about will be extra important on Wednesday. Seems the Chemo has gotten the best of my hair, and it is indeed starting to come out. Although I know I could probably wait a little longer to see how this will play out, my preference is to grab onto whatever part of the process I can control and go ahead and do the buzz.

When it began in the shower yesterday, I felt very sad, even though I knew it would happen and I planned for it to happen. Now that it's happening, I don't want it to happen—but whether I like it or not, it's going to happen, anyway. So there ya go. Let's make it happen.

Of course, the weather has been less than nice and not very predictable, so I will do my best to make a "plan." I'd love it to go like this: people (whoever wants to be and can get here) will show up about 6:30 in the evening. We can have a fire going out on the patio, and if anyone feels like bringing snacks or something, that would be fine. At 7 o'clock, we can have a little ceremony. I know that at least one or two people will have something to say or to read, and if Spirit moves anyone to participate in this way, that would be great. I really have no expectations. For me, it's more about holding space for whatever might emerge.

And then we will bring out the scissors and the clippers and let the birds have some building materials.

If the weather does not cooperate, then we all shmoosh into the house and make it work anyway. Either way, Wednesday is a big day at my house.

It's easy to admit that vanity certainly does play a role in this scenario. As I mentioned in an earlier post, I'm not sure I know a woman out there who is confident that she will look her very best with no hair on her head. What is playing a bigger part in this one for me, though, is that this is one more thing, one more way that Cancer is having a voice in what happens with and to my body. There are days when I feel completely physically mutilated, and I get sad about what this Cancer has done and is still doing to me. Then I go back to my "touchstone," my gratitude, and count the hundreds of things that Cancer cannot touch, that Cancer cannot reach. I still have everything I need to be happy and to thrive each and every day of my life.

I am still me.

Cancer can affect my Spirit for moments at a time, but I will not let it come close to breaking my Spirit today or any other day, with or without breasts and with or without hair.

I am still me.

If you live close enough and you'd like to come, please check your schedule and pop on over. It would be helpful for you to call or email so I have an idea of who is coming.

One more step on the adventure of life . . .

Hugs,
Sheri

> Cancer can affect my Spirit for moments at a time, but I will not let it come close to breaking my Spirit today or any other day, with or without breasts and with or without hair.

Chapter Eleven
My Biggest Challenge to Date

Thursday, May 13, 2010 9:33 AM, EDT

How Scott and I
responded...

Finding words to even begin to describe last night may very well be my biggest challenge to date.

By 6:30, people were indeed starting to show up. It was cold outside, and Scott was working hard to get a worthy fire going. Thankfully, it did not look like rain, so little by little, the energy was beginning to build out on the back patio for my very special evening.

Corky, my dear friend and an amazing spiritual leader, began to create the sacred space to hold the gathering circle. He burned sage, got out his drum, and slowly began to sound out the perfect heartbeat. There were 25 or 30 people, and as everyone quieted down, Corky invited us all to join hands. The circle had formed, and each and every person was absolutely present.

We had positioned a bar stool right by the fire and that is where I sat, patiently waiting to hear what would be said prior to my finding the courage to buzz off my quickly thinning hair. If I'd had any doubts about whether or not I was doing the right thing, the answer had come to me while in the shower that morning. I'd hardly been able to get the shampoo out of my hair, because every time I ran my fingers through, all I'd gotten were large fistfuls of hair, and the bathtub seemed to be covered with my locks. I was doing the right thing, and it was about to happen . . . and soon.

Corky was the most eloquent, insightful, and sensitive I've ever experienced him as he called to this circle in the spirit of unity and community for this special common purpose. I did my best to look around and find each face. I wanted to know where everyone was because each person here offered their own unique means of support, their own source of strength, and their own special relationship to me. I had to keep reminding myself to breathe.

Mary Anne is another community leader and teacher. She spoke beautifully into the circle about illness, healing, and the many meanings attached to hair and shearing. As she was speaking, I could feel my own anxiety begin to heighten and I was feeling myself getting ready.

Corky said that he wanted to shave his head, too, and he let me do his first. I'd never done this before, and it was a little scary and a lot of fun. He sat smiling while we did the deed, and I could feel my own sense of calm filling in the anxious spaces. Our laughter helped ease my tension as I got ready for my turn.

Scott had the honors of taking the clippers to me, and let me tell you that for me, this was the ultimate demonstration of trust. I have trusted this man with my life on the back of a tandem for thousands of miles. To ride on the back of a bike, having no control of virtually anything, is one of the most subservient positions to be in. Can't see, can't steer, can't brake—you get it. Now I was trusting him to take off my hair . . . and to still love me when it was all said and done. He didn't seem nervous at all. He was joking and delaying and I finally said, "Just do it!"

And so it began.

Honestly, the worst part was that my hair was blowing and falling into my face. Shaun, my older son, was so sweet, wiping my face and even getting some hairs off my tongue. Scott did most of it, and then Shaun really wanted to participate, so he finished. Scott then gave me a giant hug and kissed me on my bald little head, and I cried.

We did it, and he still loves me. I could feel his acceptance and his love.

I am still me.

Before I knew it, people were everywhere! Somebody gave me a mirror, somebody else was rubbing my head, and we were hugging and laughing and crying and hugging and crying and being cold. My mom brought me a hat. That fast, I felt so much less vulnerable, so much stronger, and, oh yes, so much warmer. I'd been cold!

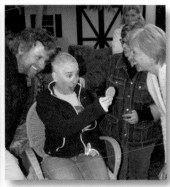

The ceremony was officially over . . . or so I thought.

A bunch of us brought the food into the house and conversations were everywhere. The hard part was done and we all wanted to visit and simply enjoy each other. I did notice that a bunch of people stayed outside, but my attention was on getting some food (I happily had a bit of an appetite, although it was just one day after Chemo). We started looking at pictures that one of my friends had taken. He is a great photographer, and I had loaded almost 400 pictures from the evening on my laptop. It was crazy to be able to relive the experience so quickly from a different perspective. Some people left and I had no idea who still remained.

But then . . .

My house was filling up again. As each person entered, I was shocked to see them coming in *without hair!* First was the photographer, who I thought had left, then more and more, and then *Scott with no hair!* I was sure he was not going to do this, yet he was smiling the biggest smile I ever saw on his face. My handsome husband had shaved his head!

There was a total of nine of us, including my girlfriend Kali (and she looks hot with very short hair), who were outside getting ready to surprise me. I am not speechless very often, but this was crazy!

The laughter and the tears continued, and I think we all were impacted deeply by the entire experience. I know I will never be the same. The lessons just keep on coming, and this one is all about acceptance and creative support.

I really don't know how to thank everyone for this one, except to tell you that I love you back and I'm proud and humbled to have so many dear, sweet friends in my life.

Lastly, how cool is this? Two of my friends are going to an event this weekend that has made a request for hair. Apparently, if you stuff hair into pantyhose, you can collect a lot of oil. So, all of the hair from shearing the nine of us will be getting shipped down to the Gulf of Mexico to help clean up the BP oil spill. I trust that there is still a ton blowing around my yard for the birds, and it feels great to know that we are also making our own small contribution to what is happening in the Gulf.

Wow, it was a big day.

> With tons of love to all of you,
> Sheri

Monday, May 17, 2010 9:06 AM, EDT

Even though I can't walk past a mirror yet without doing a double take at the woman looking back at me, there is a certain level where I'm starting to get used to this new state of being.

The ceremony from Wednesday evening is still resonating quite deeply with me. I continue to be in awe of how powerful it was to allow so much vulnerability in the center of my loving and caring community. I've spent the past couple of decades quite intentionally getting to know myself, so I typically know both what I need and how to ask for whatever it is. I've spoken before about what it means to me to have such a high level of awareness around what is happening and what my personal experience is. The other night proved to me more than ever how important it is to use that awareness as a tool to move into action.

There were actually lots of choices in my bucket about what to do when my hair started to go. We all have choices every day about what to do about hundreds of things, right? So I dug down deep and thought long and hard about which choice would best support my most fundamental needs in the moment. I needed to feel safe. I wanted to feel in control. I needed to feel accepted. I wanted to face my fears—and there were lots of fears. But more than anything, I didn't want to feel isolated or alone. The logical choice was to do exactly what we did, and the further I get away from the ceremony, the more grateful I am that we did it.

You've heard me say this before and I will continue to repeat it over and over every day of my life: *whatever we pay attention to will grow.* It doesn't serve me or anyone around me to focus on what I don't have or what is aggravating. Now please don't think I'm turning all Pollyanna or anything. Recognizing and solving problems has to be part of my daily life. In fact, it's what I get paid to do. Looking to solutions will always serve any of us in a positive way. I guess what I'm continuing to learn, continuing to affirm, is just how powerful it is to put my greatest focus on what is working and what I want more of. If I look for possibility, I find possibility. If I look for obstacles, I find more obstacles. At the end of the day, it all boils down to a couple of simple things: What do I want? And how am I going to get it?

My sister was in town this weekend, and she was so excited when I started to go outside yesterday morning with no hat. She'd been worried I'd be cold, and I had forgotten I was bald! I guess that is at least one sign that I'm integrating this phase of my process. I'm also certain that if I had hidden in my bathroom and asked Scott to take the clippers to my head in private, my current experience would not be as positive.

Please don't get me wrong: this is not fun and I'm not all "one with my bald head" quite yet. I am traveling this week to a big business meeting, and I've tried on 32 outfits with every head covering, hat, scarf, and now wig that I own, trying to imagine how I will feel the least uncomfortable. I looked up the government's website for air travel so I would know what the rules are for going through airport security, and I cry sometimes just thinking about how visible my Cancer is now to anybody who sees me. Yet . . . I won't let me stay there. I listen instead to the voices telling me that I look like a warrior. I find comfort in my new Harley hat, and I keep trying on clothes and scarves and trusting that once I walk in the door at the meeting, I will be fine. I can manage my anxieties and my fears by seeing myself on the other side of them. And that is where I will continue to put the majority of my energy.

Today is a good day . . .

Love to
you,
Sheri

Tuesday, May 18, 2010 5:43 PM, EDT

Today was hard.

Cancer sucks. Chemo sucks. Headaches suck. Expanders suck. Passing out on the bathroom floor sucks. These prickly little hairs left on my head suck. The rest of the prickly little hairs that are falling out and making Brillo pads in the shower suck. Having no appetite sucks. Wigs suck. Feeling unpredictably bad on my week off from Chemo sucks. Being really tired sucks.

It's a good thing:

> I was able to rest a little today.

It's a gift that:

> I was able to have a few great coaching calls today.

I'm so blessed to have:

> The best husband
> A supportive team
> Great clients
> An awesome family
> Generous and loving friends
> A dog that loves to nap with me
> People to cry with
> Lots of encouragement
> Phone calls, cards, emails, and posts

Okay, I feel better.

One thing I can count on is that tomorrow is another day.

Whew!

Saturday, May 22, 2010 3:54 PM, EDT

Kirk and I, fully participating

Considering that Tuesday was clearly the hardest day I've had since I began my Chemo, I think it was quite the miracle that I had the strength, energy, or even desire to get on a plane Wednesday afternoon. But boy, I really felt good on Wednesday. I got up very slowly and allowed extra caution with everything. No workout, a not-too-hot shower, just a little food at a time, and a ton of water. I had this mental checklist for the first couple of hours, and I paid very close attention to what was happening in my mind and with my body.

What was most truly helpful came from Rachael on Tuesday during one of my meltdowns. We were on the phone and she wanted to be very sure that I wouldn't push too hard to do anything. Rach is my dear friend and partner in crime at my job, and we are both quite protective of each other. As much as she wanted me at our meeting, her first priority was to make sure I was making the best decisions for my health. Her gift to me was to help me see that even if I did feel good enough to travel, I still needed to create a lot of room in my brain to allow for some flexible thinking around my time in Kansas City. It was sort of like when I broke my Chemo into two groups of four. Rach was helping me break this trip into pie pieces and giving me permission to eat only one little bite or the entire thing if I felt up to it. She

> Knowing that I could have ongoing choices just a little bit at a time was more helpful than you can imagine.

offered to drive me back and forth twenty times from her house to the meeting space if that was what I wanted or needed. We also agreed that I would be realistic about that first bite—getting on the plane at all.

Knowing that I could have ongoing choices just a little bit at a time was more helpful than you can imagine.

I don't know that I've ever been a "black and white" kind of thinker. Yet during this whole process, my learning to live in and embrace the "grey" has been incredibly important. In fact, I think it's been the key to my sanity.

There is not a lot of room for dogma or certainty when no day has any level of predictability. It's an interesting tension to sit in, when I don't know if I can plan a trip or even respond to a wedding invitation with any level of confidence that I'll be able to go. The most ironic part of this is that I never have had any level of certainty or predictability when I made plans. Of course, I created the perfect illusion of certainty, but life can always change in a heartbeat by any one of thousands of scenarios. The only difference now is that my eyes are open wider to the potential for an "interruption." None of us ever has any level of predictability, but we also can't live in fear of that fact.

It would be so easy to lock me up in my house and stop my life until all of this is over. I could pretend that when I'm done with Chemo and my final surgery, everything could go back to "normal." And we all know that I would be crazy. Life has to continue, *especially* in the face of adversity. Some things will work out and other things won't. So what? I can celebrate what works and deal with the disappointments when I have to.

It feels so good to report that this week ended on a high note, with my trip being a huge success. I'm so proud of our team for hosting an incredible workshop for our dental practices, with the most participants in the history of our organization. My energy was high, and thankfully, I was able to fully participate.

It was challenging and emotional for me to be person to person and face to face with my team and my community, thanks to my new bald head. I suffered from what I'm calling *anticipatory anxiety*—knowing that I would have really hard moments, especially with certain people, for no rational reason. So I spent literally hours thinking about what to wear on my head that would help me feel the least naked while being in my community. I had one wig, two hats, and three scarves with me so that I would have some choices, and I survived. As usual, the anxiety I had prior to showing up was much harder than the actual experience. People were loving, caring, and beautifully supportive and accepting. It didn't take long for me to be at the front of the room and comfortable back in my own skin, facilitating and participating in the event.

> As usual, the anxiety I had prior to showing up was much harder than the actual experience. People were loving, caring, and beautifully supportive and accepting.

I want to publicly thank Kirk, Rachael, and everybody who was there, for two things. First, thanks for putting on a great program and supporting the vision of our community. Second, thank you for once again putting your arms around me and holding me up, even when I know it is hard for you.

The face of Cancer is not a pretty one. Knowing that you are seeing someone you love wearing a pretty scarf to cover the evidence makes my heart hurt. Putting on a Pink Ribbon Sheri Kay pin is a loving and sweet, caring gesture, but I also look forward to the day when they can be a cool memento of the past and they are safely put away.

In the meantime, *Hineni*.

I'm grateful for what we accomplished together this past week, and I am ready for whatever comes next.

Blessings,
Sheri

Chapter Twelve
Continuation

Thursday, May 27, 2010 8:55 PM, EDT

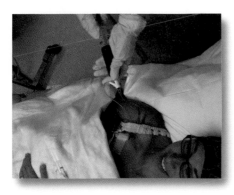

Chemo number three
in the "Sheri Kay Unit"

One of the most challenging aspects of this entire adventure is facing the daily reality that after spending 48 years as the epitome of the Energizer Bunny, I have somehow trans-mutated into an even balder version of Yertle the Turtle. I understood that there would be a lot of learning here, but it simply didn't compute that one of my lessons would be on moving in slow motion and dealing with fatigue.

I'm still so grateful to have just enough business calls to keep my mind working and my own sense of achievement tickled. I don't know what I'd do if all I had to do in between naps was nap some more! I am basically fully functional as a coach without having to leave my couch. My calls are nicely timed so that I can rest in between, and thanks to Skype, I've even been able to attend a few team meetings this week. I gain so much energy from my interactions with clients, and I appreciate so much the flexibility and support I am getting from them.

For me, "work" is healing, yet I know that many people don't experience it that way. If I could make a wish for everyone, it would be that the place we earn our living is also the place where we can be energized, fulfilled, and appreciated, the place where we can have a strong sense of belonging. Maybe I live in some kind of la-la land, but this is my reality, so I know that it's possible. And as I work with teams every day, I hope I can help them learn how to develop a culture based on personal and professional growth, collaboration, clear expectations, and, most importantly, a common purpose.

For me and those around me, our common purpose for now is to help get me healthy, and it's a crazy powerful experience to have such an incredible village around to make it happen.

My oncology team was extra fantastic this week for Chemo treatment number three. My little port that is supposed to make my treatments easier was being very temperamental. After two needle sticks, my nurse decided that laying me flat on a table instead of in their version of a La-Z-Boy chair might work. And it did! The nurses have officially named one of the suites the Sheri Kay Unit, and it will be on reserve for me when they need to get a blood return, which is the lingo for pulling back a bit on the syringe to draw a little blood from the vein into the IV line. It's how they make sure the port is still working. Once again, my mom was at my side, and one more treatment is behind us.

According to my oncologist, the next treatment (the fourth of the first four) will be the last "really hard" one. Seems the next four aren't as toxic, and I should feel much better. So my eye is on the carrot, and it will be great to complete this first phase.

Once again, I thank you for your encouragement. Even in the most challenging moments, I know I am never alone.

> As always,
> Sheri

Tuesday, June 1, 2010 6:13 PM, EDT

Continuation:
New Life

As I move through each day, it becomes more and more obvious that very little can be "certain" for any of us. In the midst of this, though, I have become very certain of at least one thing for myself: every single moment and every single event absolutely prepares me in some way for what is going to happen next. Now I can't say that it's easy to pay perfect attention. I don't think it's possible to be *that* attentive to all the potential lessons that are being taught. What I can tell you is that as I look back over the past few years, there are many, many things that were happening that helped me somehow "prepare" for my current reality.

It was Labor Day 2006 when Scott and I made our annual trip to the Midwest Tandem Rally with a few of our cycling friends. We were somewhere in Iowa, and one thing I vividly remember was corn on one side and beans on the other for lots and lots of miles! We kept getting lost, had plenty of laughs, and enjoyed putting 100-and-some miles on our bike that weekend. That trip is also embedded in my brain because of a very special couple we met. In many ways, they changed my life.

Kent and Jenny had come to this rally from Oregon because Kent was a sales rep with one of the tandem companies. We struck up a conversation the first night we were there and ended up riding the majority of our miles together over the next two days. One of the things I noticed when we were riding was that they both had the same tattoo on their left leg, and I wanted to know the story.

This couple had known a nineteen-year-old woman who had been diagnosed with a severe form of Cancer. Larisa found both peace and spiritual healing through a symbol of the Tao that means *Continuation or New Life*. She was able to come to terms with her impending "death" through a belief that her life would not be ending, that she was instead simply going on to whatever came next. Larisa wore the symbol as a tattoo, and soon other people, including her mother, followed her example. Some got the tattoo in honor of Larisa, and some for other reasons, perhaps their own connections to Cancer or in memory of loved ones.

I can't explain why, but this story deeply affected me. I was inspired by the philosophy, and I felt an undeniable connection to this young woman. As a result, I was compelled to get the tattoo myself. Scott decided he wanted it, too, and so did my younger son, Cory. We made the appointment, and all three of us were going to have this done.

It was January 2007. Cory and I were on our way, and Scott was meeting us at the tattoo store. My phone rang . . . It was the doctor's office informing me that I had just flunked my first mammogram. I certainly didn't think this was a good omen!

We did get the tattoo, and that was the first day of my realization that my life would never be the same. Although my diagnosis at that time was benign, it was the first of many scares before I got to where I am today. I share this symbol with hundreds of people now, and we all carry our important and personal stories along with it.

The following year, Kent was diagnosed with Cancer. Jenny is an amazing woman and was able to keep her physical and virtual communities up to date with Kent's treatments, progress, successes, and struggles along the way. She gave me a peek in the window about how to share what is happening and ask for and receive support. We had only met once, and yet the caring we have for them is real and my feelings for them are very special. I think of them every single day. It was only weeks after Kent's passing that I received my own diagnosis.

As I get to the end of this post, it's important that I assure you . . . Breast Cancer is not taking my life. Not now, anyway! We caught it early. We

have been aggressive both surgically and with Chemo, and every day I
am one step closer to my next adventure. I guess for me, today is about
acknowledging and appreciating just a couple of the many teachers I
have had along the way.

Friday, June 4, 2010 11:41 PM, EDT

There are certain sentences that a patient does not like hearing. "I've
never seen this happen before" is one of them. Here we go again . . .

Today was supposed to be a routine trip to my favorite plastic surgeon.
No big deal. Easy saline fill for the boobage. Actually, an "over-fill," as the
final ritual to keep me in a holding pattern until my exchange for
permanent breast implants. We had planned for that to happen just a
few weeks after my eighth and last Chemo treatment. Since the universe
seems to enjoy throwing me curveballs, today was exactly the opposite
of routine.

These temporary implants (expanders) are round and made of some
kind of plastic or silicone or something. They are supposed to be
smooth. Well, my right one has some kind of fold or ripple or bendiness
that is creating a pokey spot under my skin. My favorite plastic surgeon
is not happy. His fear is that the expander will actually rupture through
the skin, and apparently that would be a bad thing. His first thought was
to schedule a little surgery to look and see and possibly repair what is
happening. His next thought was recognizing that doing said procedure
poses some significant risks. And, he's "never seen this happen before."
I guess I should feel special, but I don't think they give gold stars for this
sort of thing. On to the next idea.

My plastic surgeon must have asked me ten times about my Chemo
timetable, and I could see his wheels turning. The best solution? Do the
exchange sooner rather than later. We were done in the treatment room,
having gone from 300cc to 400cc of saline in each side, so we went into
the private office to stare at our schedules. As much as I would have

preferred to bond with my bigger-than-ever new boobage, we were quite busy finding a time that would work to have this surgery. Before I knew it, Donna, my patient coordinator, was on the phone to the surgery center, and we set a date. June 24 is when I lose my training wheels and get to have the real deal.

This does mean that my Chemo treatments will take a short sabbatical and my new end date will be the middle of August instead of the beginning. All in all, I'm really happy with how the chain of events is playing out. The whole feeling of an extra-tight underwire bra has been gone for a while, but the expanders are still pretty uncomfortable. My understanding is that the regular implants will be way better and much more natural looking and feeling, both inside and out.

My homework is to keep moving the area where the tissue is being "poked." I should move the skin a little one way or the other, then use tape to keep it there for a while, then move it again. This should help minimize the chances of having the skin actually rupture. I can do this, no problem.

Thankfully, I have a couple of trips coming up that will keep me perfectly distracted. Tomorrow, Scott and I will drive to Chicago for a reunion with my team from the Guatemala Mission trip. You may remember that I got my diagnosis while I was on the trip in February, so seeing everyone will be wonderful. So much has happened since then! It seems like a hundred years ago. I'm also looking forward to working with a very special new dental team just outside Asheville, North Carolina.

I'm reminding myself to stay focused on what is good and how far I have come. It's so easy for my thoughts to get crazy and have my anxiety go up. I have to breathe. I have to smile. I have to laugh. The hardest part is over. *There is more behind me than I have ahead of me with surgeries and with treatment.* I am okay.

My big thanks today go to my plastic surgeon. I am truly blessed to be in your care and thank you for your time, attention, understanding, and compassion. I can't imagine doing any of this without you. My wish is that every patient could feel the level of trust and appreciation that I feel for you.

The hardest
part is over.

Monday, June 7, 2010 9:12 PM, EDT

It really is like standing at the ocean, just where the water meets the shore. Some are tiny splashes that barely get my toes wet, while others are giant rolling waves that wash over my entire body. I'm never sure when it will happen, yet I'm always right there, right at the edge, knowing that at any time I may be getting drenched.

The night of my hair ceremony, I didn't cry until just after Scott finished with the clippers. Once he looked me right in the eyes and I could see he was okay, the wave came from way down inside, and I think my tears flowed from a combination of relief and feeling completely accepted and loved. I don't know that I had ever felt that particular emotion before, and it took some time to swell and move through my body before it released.

In my work, we often talk about helping patients learn to come to terms with their own loss of different measures of health. We help them recognize and move through their grief process, and we also support them as they explore new possibilities for a higher level of health. As much as I joke around about getting old, I have been very fortunate in that I have not faced any significant health issues until now. I hate that I have limitations with my energy, my appetite, and my ability to plan. So, it's obviously no surprise that at any time of any day I experience my own sense of loss, my own sense of grief. And it's the people around me who help me cope and come to terms with where I am now and the new possibilities that I have in the future.

On Friday, I drove about an hour away, where I knew some of my friends would be attending a lecture. I hadn't seen most of them since my hair loss, and it's still very hard for me to expose myself, especially to people I care about. I am certainly not "one with my wig," so most of the time I wear either a hat or a scarf. Even though I've posted bald pictures online as a way to sort of warn people and also help me get more comfortable with me, I still feel very vulnerable right now with this.

It was lunchtime and a woman I've known for a few years was so kind and told me that my "pictures were amazing" and I "look sooo beautiful." I could see the sincerity in her eyes and feel the love from her heart. I could also feel the wave begin to bubble up inside all the way from my toes to my nose. I thanked her and hugged her and also had to tell this angel of a woman that I wished I could see myself the way she saw me in that moment.

Probably the biggest challenge I have is accepting how much I have not been able to do this year, like ride my bike or travel as much as I'm used to. For years I've been wanting to teach at the Pankey Institute on Key Biscayne, and I was finally offered the chance to do just that for a Team Enhancement course two weeks from now. Well, that's a Chemo week, and I had to decline. I was thrilled to be helping my good friend process some ideas for a lecture he will deliver at that course, when out of nowhere I felt another one of those waves building up in my throat. I am so sad that I won't be there to hear him, to support him.

I wouldn't be human if I weren't experiencing my grief along with my gratitude, and I think it's important to paint a full picture of what goes on inside for me. It's also fair to say that my waves are only a small part of my days. I open my heart to the moments when they emerge and give myself permission to cry, to feel sad, to grieve, and to be afraid. As I look back over this experience as a whole, I guess the best news is that I've never felt as though I was drowning.

I've never felt as though I was drowning.

Chapter Thirteen
Slowing Down Enough to See
How Far We've Come

Experience has taught me that when I am about to do something that feels really, really big, the anxiety that comes before doing it is far worse than the thing itself. I always get *very* nervous before I speak in front of large groups. I feel sick before I sing in public. My hands shake and I doubt my own ability just before I begin doing my work with teams. And then I begin to do that really, really big thing. My pulse slows, my breathing evens out, my hands stop shaking, and I do it. I do whatever "it" is, and then I'm always surprised that I did okay. Over and over again, I surprise myself. And now it is happening again.

This is a big week for me, the halfway point of my Chemo. So much has happened since my diagnosis in February, it's hard to believe how many appointments and procedures have been completed. It feels amazing to look back and see how far we have all come, and for the first time in months, I can see the light at the end of this tunnel. I hesitate to make this sound too easy, considering all of the glitches that have emerged in my matrix. But I also feel confident when I state that my current treatment plan/to-do list is really and truly getting shorter.

Two weeks from today I will be finishing breast reconstruction. Expanders out and breast implants in. I'm not sure if I talked about this before or not, but in case you didn't know . . . *nipples are optional.* My God-given ones were removed during the mastectomy because I had *ductal carcinoma*, and nipples are part of the ductal system. If I choose to have them "made," it will be yet another surgery down the road. For now, I'm focusing on the mandatory stuff, and the optional things feel very unimportant.

My oncologist wants to wait four weeks post surgery before we begin the last four Chemo treatments, and that works great for me. I can recover from surgery, do some work travel during the break, and it shouldn't feel like too big a deal to go back for that final four.

I remember a while back I wrote about short-term goals and long-term vision. That philosophy, that concept, that plan, is what got me to this day in the best possible way. In all honesty, my head is constantly spinning about what is happening, how many more treatments, when I can travel, if I can ride my bike, how much I can work, staring at my calendar, thinking about everything over and over. And then I regain my sanity as I come back to those most important little steps—my short-term goals.

> Short-term goals and long-term vision . . . That philosophy, that concept, that plan, is what got me to this day in the best possible way.

There are no words to describe all the levels of anxiety that I have reached since the day of my diagnosis. My life and my emotions have been nothing short of a roller coaster. Yet *Hineni*, here I am! I am over the hump! Barring more interruptions or any big surprises, I have far less ahead of me than I have behind me. And today, my friends, I am very relieved.

Thanks for walking every step with me.

Friday, June 11, 2010 2:15 PM, EDT

Sharing stories with Mr. Froman

It's a beautiful gift and a humbling experience to know how many people are out there following what is happening for me right now. Every single one of us has a story, and as my friend reminded me this morning, none of them is a short story. The question burning for me today is about how often I slow down enough to really be interested, curious, and engaged in other people's stories. After all, isn't that where we can make the deepest connection? Each one of us longs to be heard, and each one of us carries inside of us the stories that helped us become the people we are today.

One of the most caring and compassionate men I have ever known is a Holocaust survivor. He is a respected elder in our Jewish community and dearly loved by many, especially my entire family. I can listen to his stories for hours, over and over again. I try to imagine him as a young boy living in the midst of such horror. Then I see him today as a kind and gentle man who always makes time to help other people, to live in service, and to spread a message of peace and hope.

Early in my treatment, Mr. Froman was wintering in Florida and called me often to offer assurance and love. Upon his return, I was blessed with a visit. I hadn't lost my hair yet, but he knew I was worried and promised me that even without hair I would still be beautiful. That day he also pulled out his little prayer book. Together we prayed. Together we cried. We could feel each other's stories, and I've honestly never felt closer to him.

This week I heard the beginning of new stories from two women I know, and I feel so sad. Both of these stories began with the news of a Breast Cancer diagnosis. I won't pretend to know how either of them feels, although I'm sure there are many similarities to how I felt when I first found out. I find it ironic that both of these women had been following my story, and I am glad they both could find comfort in talking with me. Hopefully I will be one of the many people they can go to for support, information, and guidance. What I'm clear about is that their story will be completely their own. We will be able to find connections and share common threads. Then, if we pay very close attention, we will also find the parts that are different, the pieces that are personal and unique and special.

We may come together through what is similar, but we will learn and grow as we look for and embrace what is different.

Today I renew my own commitment to slow down long enough to really hear the stories that are being told. All of our stories are important.

Friday, June 18, 2010 9:44 PM, EDT

It seems that at the end of each and every week, I'm reflecting on how big it felt. This week is definitely no exception, and I do think for lots of reasons it was extra big.

Even though I have been back to traveling for a while, the amount of work I've been responsible for has been pretty easy from an energy perspective. But this week, I began with a new team in North Carolina, and the amount of energy it took for me to get to know them and present material for a full two days was significant. This is the kind of work that wore me out when I was healthy!

It's a funny sort of experience in that it can both energize and drain me at the same time. Yet that is exactly what happens when I do what I do.

When I first began this kind of work, I would come home feeling so sad because I had to leave the people I was enjoying so much. My handsome husband would tell me I was guilty of becoming "too attached." He didn't like seeing me go through the "downs."

I would argue back that it was absolutely worth it, because I so valued the relationships we were creating. The more I got used to the "cycles," the less I would go through what I now know was a grieving period. I learned to create ways to stay closely connected, and then I didn't feel so bad about leaving. Today, for the first time in years, I find myself in that familiar place of grief about leaving a team, and I also find myself touching a few other pieces of grief I've probably been ignoring.

The North Carolina team was incredible, and the hospitality from the dentist and his beautiful wife was one of the most special I can ever remember. I could write a whole book just on them and their magical Treehouse up on the mountain! As I reflect on our time together, one of the things that made it rather *intense* for me was knowing that everyone on the team had been reading this journal online.

On one hand, it was freeing, as each person was so accepting and kind. When I arrived at the office, it was as if each team member already knew me, and they wore pink ribbons in my honor. We laughed and cried and shared stories. They asked and I answered questions about both process and experience. They told me about their own connections to Cancer, survival, and even loss. I felt so connected to each of them so quickly. It shouldn't have been any surprise, because they'd already been looking for weeks through the window I have been painting directly to my soul.

On the other hand, it was as if I were standing there perfectly naked, with not a shred of me hiding. I made a decision months ago to put my story and my life out there in the open for anyone to see, and I'm still certain I made the right choice. I wanted to be seen, I wanted to be heard, and I wanted to provide a forum for people I care about to stay connected to everything happening. Yet, being seen can sometimes be so very hard. Experiencing such a profound level of intimacy left me feeling both wonderful and raw all at the same time.

Keep in mind that in the midst of what I'm describing, the team and I were fully involved in a two-and-a-half-day training session designed to help them make significant organizational changes over the course of the next twelve months. This "program" in and of itself is an emotional, intellectual, mental, and even physical challenge. We all were learning, growing, and planning together. Did I mention that this was a little intense? You betcha! And I loved it. I was challenged, focused, and proud of all of us for what we were able to accomplish.

It's no wonder, though, that traveling home and not finding my own bed until nearly one in the morning left me more than a bit tired today. I had calls to make and emails to catch up on, and I struggled to find the wind in my sails. Every little while I'd try to rest, but those waves I talked about a while back were sneaking up on me. I found myself in tears more than once, with the biggest rush coming not long after Scott got home from work. I was in touch with the sadness of leaving such a special experience with the team, and I was so tired that I felt kinda sick. My head hurt, and my belly was icky. I knew I would have to cancel dinner with some close friends.

Scott asked why I was crying and all I could say was that I felt this awful grief. Grief for not being able to keep my dinner plans. Grief for my hair. I had a fleeting moment of not wanting to do any more Chemo and felt grief for losing the boundless energy that had always defined me. As excited as I am about my final breast surgery next week, I had a wave of grief for the loss of my old saggy ones that were not numb from being destroyed. I looked at Scott and rubbed his nearly bald head. Every time I look at him, I'm reminded how much he showed me his love by shaving his head the night he buzzed my own hair off.

And then . . . the wave was gone.

Sunday, June 20, 2010 2:13 PM, EDT

As I look ahead, I already know that this week is going to be a good one. I've had plenty of rest, enjoyed a great day taking a convertible ride in the country with Scott, and had breakfast with my mom and dad to celebrate Father's Day.

What seems most important is that I've really turned a corner about where I am in this entire process. What should be my final surgery is on Thursday, and then all I have left is four Chemo treatments. Realistically, I'm certain that I passed the halfway point a while back, but there was no way I could know or see that at the time.

As I move into this week (obviously barring any major interruptions), I can vividly see what has been an elusive light at the end of this crazy tunnel.

I can absolutely do this. One surgery. Four treatments. The icing on the cake is that surgery gives me a nice break from Chemo. I've not worried for a minute that this means I will finish a little later in the summer. I'm clear about the benefits of this "plan."

First, I will finally be rid of these stupid expanders! I guess I should be grateful for them, as they were a means to an end, helping to stretch the needed amount of skin for the installation of my new boobage. I appreciate that they did their job. I'm also really looking forward to having the silicone that they tell me will be far more comfortable and also much more natural in feel and look. It will be a bonus to land on a final size so I can figure out my wardrobe.

It is fascinating how the surgery will go. Once they put me under general anesthesia, my favorite plastic surgeon will make about a three-inch incision along the original mastectomy line. He will "pop" the expanders, let all the saline out, and remove them. Then, the fun begins. He has ordered three different-sized implants, and the doctor, along with the surgical team, will start to experiment. It will be up to the team to determine which size produces the best aesthetic result. I was told they will actually sit me up during the process, which makes perfect sense. It's most important that these "breasts" look right when I'm sitting up rather than when I'm lying down. It does feel a bit odd that a roomful of strangers will be making these decisions without me. Talk about an exercise in surrender and trust!

The second benefit from this plan is that I get a break from Chemo! Having a treatment every two weeks has been a tough routine. I've loved being able to count on the off weeks to feel good and do what I want. And yet, as soon as I feel good, it's time for Chemo again. This break will be so important for me both physically and emotionally. I will have my next treatment on July 20 and will do my best to sneak in some fun between surgical recovery and then. This feels sooo good.

I certainly don't want to cross my fingers too tightly that there won't be any surprises. Whatever is supposed to happen will happen. For today, I know that all is well, and I'm looking forward to each and every day of this week.

With my ongoing love and gratitude to each of you and a Happy Father's Day to my dad and all the dads out there,

Sheri

Thursday, June 24, 2010 8:04 PM, EDT

Surgery is on the "ta-done" list!

It was a great day, filled with a couple of nice surprises. The original surgery time was moved to 8 in the morning. The earlier the better for me, although it meant that Mom and I were on the road at 6:15. Neither one of us got much sleep last night, but that was okay. We had plenty of time to nap later in the day.

The procedure was at a surgery center about 45 minutes away, and this was our first experience there. The entire team was so good, from the girl who checked us in to the pre-op nurse who let me know that she was the one who'd spoken with me the day before. Having even a hint of familiarity in a strange place, especially before surgery, was very comforting. Medical history reviewed? Check. IV started? Check. Mom is allowed back? Check. Listen to music to calm down? Check. My favorite plastic surgeon shows up? Yay!

It's almost funny that it felt perfectly natural to stand with my gown pulled down to my waist with a nurse and my Mom watching as my surgeon sat, eyes to my bare chest. Using his purple marker, he began to outline landmarks, highlight incision lines, and find my midline. (After all, my new cleavage will need to be centered.) We talked about possibilities and limitations and hopeful outcomes, with one fact being that I will not be symmetrical. He wanted to be sure that I knew that going in, and I'm fine with it. The "Cancer side" was far more radical in its surgical destruction, and it would be very challenging to get them even. Most people have feet that are different sizes, right? I'll find out more when the bandages come off and the swelling goes down. I'm honestly not worried. In the grand scheme of things, it's simply not a priority.

The team's attention to detail was awesome. They talked with each other and with me to make sure I was comfortable and an active participant in what was happening. I love when people do that. I mentioned I wished I could watch, and one of the nurses actually took a couple of pictures during the surgery for me. She included them with my post-op instructions. Another nurse heard me say that I hated being intubated and assured me that I didn't have to be. I thought general anesthesia always meant intubation. Guess not! Immediately I was more relaxed, and at that point I could feel myself fading off to sleepy land.

Next thing I remember, I was sitting in a La-Z-Boy with a warm blanket and some apple juice. Mom was signing papers and going to get the car. Everything certainly seemed to be moving fast for me to leave, but off we went and made it home before noon.

The rest of that day was all about sleeping, with a little food and liquid and some phone calls in between. It's now been 24 hours, and I have NO pain. Not even a small amount of discomfort. I'm bound pretty tight, so we will see what happens when we unwrap me tomorrow at my post-op visit. I'm certainly not complaining, but I did expect I'd feel something.

Thanks to friends for bringing me dinner and for popping over for a visit and some Kodak moments. Biggest thanks to Mom for walking another big step with me today. By the time this is over, we will have completed a marathon, sure and steady—a very long marathon. I love you, Mama.

Friday, July 2, 2010 10:10 AM, EDT

Scott has been working on the mother of all projects at our house for two summers in a row. He began with a lot of demolition to our existing steps, sidewalk, and small back patio. He has continued by pouring a huge, new patio, new back steps, and a new sidewalk, along with building a magnificent outdoor kitchen. Scott created sitting walls, a bench around a new fire pit, a built-in grill, and a "bar" to sit along, and he cut and placed each and every stone himself. In the midst of the construction, we also had many tons of dirt delivered so that he could level out the back side of our property, and he has been tilling, raking, and finally planting new grass in that entire area. The work he has completed, along with his job and taking care of me, boggles my brain.

The thing that I find curious is the lens through which he sees his project. When we go out there together, or especially when people come over, the feedback is awesome and positive and all focused on how much has been done and how beautiful it looks. Scott's conversation is always about the details that could be different and the vision he has of what is yet left to complete. For me, I think it's important to celebrate what is done—I mean, really take in and appreciate how far this has come. Don't get me wrong, I know there is still a ton to do. That list is long. I just want to revel in the pieces that are done and wonderful and beautiful before going into the next series of projects.

And that's where I am today in my own project, really celebrating how far I've come in the past six months—how far we've all come.

Strategically:

- January: I flunked my mammogram.
- February: Biopsy, trip to Guatemala, diagnosis
- March: Double mastectomy/begin reconstruction
- April: Surgical placement of port/begin Chemo/surgical repair from infection
- May: Hair loss/community ceremony
- June: Complete breast reconstruction

I never did experience even a twinge of discomfort after this last surgery, and the doctor gave me a clean bill of implant health, with no more physical restrictions. I can exercise, ride my bike, or go fishing. Whatever I want! I still get tired a little quickly, so I will take it easy. But I can do anything!

Emotionally:

Oh, what a ride it has been! On any given day, especially early on, I could go from laughter to tears in a nano-second. Cancer is now part of my daily life, thoughts, actions, and learning. I've experienced more love and joy than I ever thought possible, and I've also gained more insight into facing fear than I ever imagined.

My body has both failed and saved me, and I appreciate my friends and family as much as I value my ability to breathe. I've learned what it means to cherish and be cherished, and I'm deepening my commitment to enjoy as many moments in each day as I can. I give myself permission to feel sadness, grief, and anger, and I challenge myself to better protect myself from emotional baggage that no longer serves me or that brings me harm. I think I'm getting more clear about what is really important in life, and I look for opportunities to let people know how special they are to me.

Today, I physically feel the best I have felt since that first big surgery in February, so I feel an extra bounce in my step as we move into this holiday weekend. My plan is to work for a while and spend as much time as I can enjoying the sunshine and the breeze.

I hope Scott can slow down for at least a little while to enjoy his patio, too.

> Love to you all,
> Sheri

Chapter Fourteen
Finding Words

Monday, July 5, 2010 10:15 PM, EDT

Daddy

I've been thinking about this post all day, and I'm still not sure how to put my words together.

You've heard a lot about my handsome husband, and not so much about the first significant man in my life, my dad. I am the baby girl in our family, and Daddy has always held the most special place in my heart. I have always craved his attention and did whatever I could as a kid to spend as much time with him as he would allow. I loved going down to "help" him work on the boat engines, and even in recent years we found things to do together, like buying the flowers for the temple or going into Cleveland with Mom to buy Passover goodies.

Dad taught me to love cars, how to parallel park, everything there is to know about being a helping hand on a boat, and, most importantly, how to live in service to help other people. With all his grumpiness, my dad has an incredibly warm heart and an amazingly generous spirit.

It's been ten years since Daddy had his first heart attack, and he has been fighting the good fight with more lives than a cat ever since. Today we turned a very difficult corner, as the wind is certainly leaving his sails.

This evening my father was transported to hospice. As a family, our goal is that he will be kept as comfortable as possible and that he will feel calm and loved.

None of us knows when our last days will be right in front of us, so I feel blessed and grateful for the conversations that our family is able to have right now in these very precious moments.

I thought the past few months had provided all the learning I could ever imagine about facing fear and finding courage. I was wrong. My father is still teaching me about both of those things.

Please keep my family in your prayers, and I promise to keep you posted.

Much love,
Sheri

Friday, July 9, 2010 8:28 AM, EDT

The family, together

Standing by his bedside yesterday morning, I asked my dad about his greatest accomplishment. With quite a little smirk and a hint of a smile, he said that it was marrying my mother. He then looked at Mom, my brother, and me and said, "I did good on that one," and laughed his devilish laugh. If anyone had asked him what he was most proud of, his answer would certainly have been "his kids."

We kept our vigil for the rest of the day, always making sure he was comfortable and attended to. Throughout the day I could see that he was fading. He stayed awake less, slept longer in the middles, and even decided by evening that he wanted a break from his oxygen.

At 9 o'clock at night, we both said, "I love you," and I left to go home. By 10 o'clock, Dad had already passed.

I've read and heard stories about how each person finds their own way when their time comes, and I believe Dad was no exception. He took care of business, said what had to be said, and did what he was ready to do. He lived and ended his life with pride and dignity, in a way that worked for him.

Our family will be together, taking care of whatever needs to be taken care of today. I can't imagine what the next few days will be like. The funeral will be on Sunday.

Thank you, as always, for your love and care.

A long time from now, I know I will be looking back at 2010, wondering how I ever made it through.

For now, I am taking each day as it comes. I am grateful that this has happened during my Chemo break, while my physical being and energy are as good as possible.

> Love to you,
> Sheri

Saturday, July 17, 2010 8:11 AM, EDT

For the past week, there is one word that has continued to resonate throughout my entire being. I honestly don't think there is a person who will dare to agree with me, and yet the word is still there, running in and out of my brain like a fly buzzing around the room. I just can't help it. I'm completely full. This year has been so much about fear, procedures, poison, change, fatigue, and stress, and as of last week I feel completely, utterly, and perfectly PATHETIC.

There, I said it. The caption under my picture, if I would let anyone take my picture, would simply read "pathetic."

It really hit me the hardest when I was sitting in a front row seat during the graveside service for my father. His coffin hadn't been lowered yet. My sister was holding my hand and the cantor began to chant. Sweat was running down my body and tears began to stream down my face. I looked up for just a moment and could see dozens of people facing me and many eyes landing on mine. It was that look of sadness and grief on their faces that got my imagination working overtime.

I could hear the chatter inside other people's heads as they looked at me. The imaginary voices were all talking about how *this would be sad all by itself, but it is even more sad and downright PATHETIC that the youngest daughter has Cancer, and in the middle of treatment she lost her dad, too.* The imaginary voices kept saying over and over again *how PATHETIC it was to look first at death, and then at Cancer crying from her chair with the little black hat and her little bald head.*

I know in my heart that we all create our own realities through the ways we respond to whatever is happening in any moment. I get that. I usually live that. I spend a good portion of my life talking to myself to reframe my own moments of unhealthy thinking. This particular reality is different in so many ways.

The true and unwavering fact is that the past six months have been the hardest of my life. Maybe it's my time to slow down, my time to feel sad, and maybe even my time to feel PATHETIC. I don't have to talk to myself every moment with the intention of reframing my thinking.

It's a good thing I believe that bad things happen in threes. I told my mom the other day, this certainly means we are done for a while. I lost my breasts. I lost my hair. And now I've lost my dad. Any way you look at it, that is a lot of loss. From my perspective, I've earned an EZ Pass through the tollbooths of my life, at least for a little while.

As I begin today, my 49th birthday, the idea of a celebration seems futile. I can go so far as to be grateful to be alive. Cancer showed up in my 49th year to kick my ass, but it certainly has not and will not kill me, at least not now. I can feel deep love and appreciation for my husband, my family, and the best friends that anyone could ask for. I am proud that my work is about positive change and relationships, that it has meaning. I love that my life is one of purpose and great intention.

So although there will be no big parties, no gatherings or hoo-ha, I will quietly move into today with as much grace and dignity as I can muster. My birthday present to myself will be that I let go of PATHETIC and move into whatever comes next. My presents from my dad came a little bit early: first, when he acknowledged that I was *always here*, and then, when he said he loved me for the very last time.

Hi. Ne. Ni.

Monday, July 19, 2010 10:15 PM, EDT

Through my sadness and my tears, I made my way to the angels in oncology at the Cleveland Clinic for my day-before-Chemo blood draw. I told them I was going on strike and let them know that I was refusing to continue treatment. They hugged me and sat with me while I cried some more, and then they assured me that quitting is not an option. One nurse talked to me while another accessed my port for the first time in six weeks.

> They hugged me and sat with me while I cried some more, and then they assured me that quitting is not an option.

A very good friend of mine helped to put language to my current experience: *I've tasted freedom from Chemo* for the past six weeks. It's harder than I could have imagined to go at it again. With my dad's passing, I clearly crossed an emotional threshold, and it's taking every bit of my reserves to stay in this game. For the first time since I can remember, I've retracted from calls and from being with people. I'm in a space that is not familiar to me. Spending time in the quiet, alone, or with just one or two people is more than enough stimulation for my mind and Spirit. I know I need to trust my inner voice to guide me to what is best. In fact, I don't think it's ever been more important for me to very carefully listen to that inner voice.

Hineni. I can be here for me. Here I am. Here I stand. And when I need to be with someone, I have more people to lean on than I can count.

The doctor gave me a new prescription for steroids, and I took my first dose about an hour ago. The instructions are to take five tonight and five in the morning. There are 40 pills in the bottle . . . enough for my final four treatments. The countdown has officially begun. As the pills go away, so will my treatments. Although a big part of me is kicking and screaming as I move into tomorrow, the bigger part of me can focus on counting down. It is all just one big mind-f*#!, right?

Please know that I am tired, and I'm more than a little scared about how I will respond to this new Chemo. I am being told that it will not be as bad as what I had before, and yet I know there are many possible side effects —hence the steroids. Until I'm in the throes of these last four, I don't know how my body will tolerate what is about to happen.

Breathing is helping. Crying is helping. Hugs are helping. Journaling is helping. Reminding myself that *I am still me* is helping.

Little bald head and all, I am still me.

> Wish me luck!
> Sheri

Chapter Fourteen
Living on the Edge

Wednesday, July 21, 2010 8:25 PM, EDT

A good friend of mine says that every once in a while it's important to do something that scares the hell out of you. The theory is that as we face our fears, we learn more about our own capacity and our potential. Some people call this our "learning edge."

I have to admit that I've always embraced finding that "edge" and reveling in the learning that follows.

I also have to admit that I've found myself on this edge so often in the past few months that I'm having huge challenges in finding enough time in between to see, let alone integrate, my learning. In my core, I know that all experiences we have offer us lessons, offer us the chance to know ourselves on a deeper level. I also have to believe that all of this is for something, for some greater good, maybe to help others in some way, or to pay off some Karmic debt. Believing there is some point or purpose in this process is one of the key things that keeps me going.

Yesterday began my final four. To say I was anxious about this treatment would be a giant understatement. Part of my fear was around the known: my past experience of the first four. I know what it is like to go to the infusion room, to have the needle stuck in my port, and to taste the metallic yuck in my mouth. I know the fatigue that followed my previous treatments, and the impact it had on my quality of life. I know that my hair, which is beginning to come back like peach fuzz, will be falling out all over again. I know that I was very happy to have NOT lost my eyebrows and they are starting to disappear.

And then there is the fear of the unknown: the risk of reaction to the new infusion, possible neuropathy in my hands and feet, losing fingernails and toenails, and not knowing what this chemistry will do to my energy. No matter how much I read or look on the Internet . . . until *my* body processes this stuff, we won't know what my reaction will be.

The infusion did go well, with just a little blip on the radar. My port was very cooperative this time. It's funny that its position in my chest is different since my breast reconstruction was completed, and that appears to be a good thing! We got blood return right away, and there was no hanging upside down or going to the special Sheri Kay suite.

Because the risk of reaction is high with this particular Chemo drug, they front-loaded me with steroids, gave me more steroids in the IV, and also gave me an IV antihistamine, a common allergy medication. I was in the first room, front and center to the nurses in the window, and they proceeded with caution, watching very carefully for me to turn red, have trouble breathing, or experience any heart racing. About ten minutes in, I began to feel very dizzy. Mom stepped just outside my door and told the nurse.

Within seconds, there were four nurses in my room. They stopped the infusion, tipped my chair back, started oxygen, and popped an O2 meter on my finger. I was thinking about two things. The first thing was that I was worried about my mom. I hated that they were putting oxygen on me just after everything we went through in the hospital and hospice with my dad. I didn't want her to be scared. Secondly, I was aware of a *lot* of faces and eyes staring down at me. I couldn't even hear their words, but I knew they were all busy figuring me out.

Seems I was not having a reaction to the Chemo. I was having a normal response to the antihistamine. Infusion was restarted and within an hour I was done. Needless to say, I slept for a good couple of hours when we got home, and Mom was sleeping on the other couch. We both needed a good rest!

There are still more unknowns as I move into the next few days, so my plan is to lie low and take it slow. I have some calls scheduled and will rest during the in-betweens.

Today, I'm able to breathe a little easier. Walking into that room yesterday scared the hell out of me. I am living on my learning edge. And I am still in this game, even though there is no doubt in my mind that this is the hardest thing I have ever done. Three more to go.

The encouragement I have gotten from my physical and virtual community has been more powerful and more helpful than ever. I'm beginning to think I have now heard from every person I have ever met in my life, and I appreciate every word, thought, and prayer.

Love and blessings to each of you,
Sheri

Sunday, July 25, 2010 10:41 PM, EDT

About to be hit by a big wave . . .

Ever since this whole thing started, my experience with time has been completely distorted. My memory is also in serious question. I know there are definite gaps in some days, and giant chunks of time are clearly missing. I joke around about having "Chemo Brain," and I'm certain there is at least some truth to that concept. I'm trying to be kind to myself and not get worried or upset about the gaps. Almost every day, I'm in conversations with different support people who make sure I know what I need to know, or I hear stories about what happened and my own memory gets jarred. Who knows, maybe some of what I'm missing will be filled in when I go back someday and read this journal!

Here's what I know today: I do and will continue to remember this weekend.

A few months ago, I heard about an event called Relay For Life. It's a Cancer walk that occurs all over the country through the American Cancer Society. I was really interested in participating in this event, and my friend, Leigh Ann, was excited to be a team captain and help get us all organized. I had thought I would be done with Chemo by now and that this walk would be somewhat of a capstone event. Thanks to a number of "interruptions," I was instead on the tail end of Chemo, number five out of eight.

I will say that from a nausea and fatigue perspective, this treatment was not bad. What totally sucked happened on Thursday, Friday, and into Saturday and even today: bad bone pain. Deep in my legs, like when I have a fever. It's this achy, *can't get comfortable and feel like crying a lot* pain. Ibuprofen wasn't doing it, so I moved on to the prescription pain medicine. Thankfully, it helped enough to make me functional. The walk was on Saturday (yesterday), and I really wanted to do my part. And then there was the heat.

I could write a book about the event itself, so let me tell you just a couple of highlights.

This was my first public support event since my diagnosis, and I was in awe of the time and energy that so many put into this Relay For Life. There were booths, food, decorations, water stations, entertainment, tons of Cancer paraphernalia, raffles, and a beautiful feeling of care and community as all of us came together for a common purpose: to see an end to this thing called Cancer. The hard part is this: I had to keep reminding myself that I, Sheri Kay, am one of the statistics. I'm one of the reasons there has to be an event. I'm one of the reasons we are searching for a Cure.

I've come to appreciate that *time* is life's greatest commodity, and lots and lots of people gave up hours and days of their lives to donate *time* to this walk. My friends and my family took time away from other things they could have been doing to, in some small way, make a difference. Thanks to each and every one of you who showed up or donated to make this work.

When it was time for the first lap, somebody asked me if I wanted to help hold up a banner. There I was, front and center, as a survivor, standing among other survivors. It was like walking in a weird dream. *How did I get here? Holding up a Cancer Survivor banner?* Then I saw my husband and my friends. I knew where I was and exactly how I got there.

The most emotional and surreal part came as the sun went down. It was time for the Luminaria Ceremony. People had been purchasing luminarias—white paper bags with a votive candle inside—all day. There were hundreds of them all lined up along the track. Each bag carried a name either in honor or in memory of someone who was loved by somebody else. At the last minute, my mom bought one. There was a luminaria with my name on it.

I'd be the first one in line to buy a bag for somebody else! This was one of those moments when I just wanted to kick my feet and turn the other way, away from the whole thing, away from Cancer itself. It was oddly chilling to stand with my mom, my husband, and my friends and stare at my own name on this thing. There are hundreds of places I'd love to put my name! On a luminaria bag at a Cancer walk would not have been my first choice. I took in a giant breath and faced my Cancer demon one more time. I breathed again and looked at my mom. Again, and looked at everybody around me. One more time, and spoke Hineni so quietly that only God could hear . . .

As we walked the track to pay respects to every luminaria around the circle, I held hands with both my mom and Scott. We walked for each other, for all the other people represented, and even though we never said it out loud, Mom and I walked for my dad.

> There are hundreds of places I'd love to put my name! On a luminaria bag at a Cancer walk would not have been my first choice. I took in a giant breath and faced my Cancer demon one more time. I breathed again and looked at my mom. Again, and looked at everybody around me. One more time, and spoke *Hineni* so quietly that only God could hear...

The entire day was filled with little waves of emotion for me. The Luminaria Ceremony was a giant rush, and then it washed away as quickly as it came.

As I sit here tonight, I am no longer in pain, and I'm looking forward to a normal week of work and travel. As I started typing this entry, Scott was watching the Tour de France in its final stage. If you haven't been paying attention, Lance is riding with Team Radio Shack, and tonight that team made my Spirit soar. Every member of the team was wearing a special jersey with the same number: 28. They dedicated today's ride to *28 million Cancer survivors*. I'm done crying now, so touched by the unrelenting commitment that so many people have to making this really bad thing go away.

In case you're wondering—I am very clear about why I will remember this weekend. This, my friends, is the weekend that I claim the title of *Survivor*. It's no longer just a word. It has become my new state of being. I think the Relay event was my initiation, and then Lance and the number 28 was the crown of affirmation.

As I say good night, I breathe in and out once again. Taking in all the strength, love, and hope you have to offer, and blowing out all that I carry that no longer serves me . . . Hi. Ne. Ni.

Chapter Sixteen
Being Normal

Okay, guess what I smell like. Shampoo!!! To be honest, I don't need it at all, with just this little bit of peach fuzz on my noggin. The truth is, I created a theme for this week and titled it "Being Normal." What I get to do in the shower is just part of the fun. I shaved my legs, used conditioner, and cracked myself up trying to imagine where, if I had nipples, they would be positioned on my new boobage. I am actually this close to getting out the magic markers just to give me a reason to laugh harder.

The idea of Being Normal for the week came to me on Sunday afternoon when I finally stopped having pain. I looked at my week's schedule and felt a smile come across my face. I had calls all day Monday, travel to Florida to work with clients on Tuesday and Wednesday, and then calls on Thursday and Friday. My days had NO doctor appointments, tests, or trips to the hospital or hospice anywhere at all.

I will be singing at the synagogue tonight for a Shabbat service, going to my niece's birthday party tomorrow, shopping with my daughter-in-law for curtains, and riding my bike with my handsome husband hopefully both Saturday and Sunday. This is exactly what I remember normal to be like on any given week in my life before I got my diagnosis.

One of the most pleasant surprises about my theme this week was that I actually opened, and began reading, a book I took with me on my trip.

Growing up, I did not read. Nothing. Not even the books I was required to read for school. It's nothing short of a miracle that I passed any classes, considering the distaste I had for books. For me, reading was one more thing other people wanted me to do that I was rebelling against. (Yes, I was a handful back then.)

It wasn't until I went back to school as an adult that I began to find a use for academics, and books began to hold a great deal of interest for me. No books, no learning. No learning, no degree. No degree, no way for me to take care of my boys. Amazing what a little motivation will do. Somewhere in that same time frame, my brother gave me a novel, and my love for reading was ignited. For many years now, I have read fast and I have read a lot.

Since my diagnosis, reading is one of the things I have not been able to do. My attention span has been short, and my ability to focus on the pages disappeared. I just told someone the other day that I have not read anything longer than an article or an email since February . . . until yesterday.

When I got on the plane to head back home, I opened a memoir that was a gift around the time of my big surgery. While packing for this trip, I had chosen it from a huge shelf filled with all the books I haven't been able to get to. Before I knew it, I was on page 50, and by the time my plane landed, I had put 100 pages behind me. I was pulled into the story and relishing every word. It was hard to put it down long enough to go to the bathroom, and I almost didn't take my sleeping pill last night because I wanted to keep reading and I didn't want to forget any parts.

Because I am still Being Normal, it was nice to take time this afternoon to sit on my patio and continue reading my book. Yes, this is Normal.

Within Normal, there have been lots of little moments when other things tried to creep in. A peek at next week's Chemo schedule, a glimpse in the mirror at my little bald head, or a look down at my hand where my dad's ring now lives on my finger—all had the potential to knock me off balance. I may have wavered a bit, and that was okay. I also found my way right back to that place of solid ground.

I like this theme, and this week. It's everything I could ever ask for.

Tuesday, August 3, 2010 4:24 PM, EDT

 My hair, wondering if it is
safe to come out yet

As I gently shift from "Being Normal" back to Chemo, I find myself sitting in an interesting tension. Part of me wants to feel excited with *the end* being so close, and another part of me is feeling very, very cautious. I really am very excited to have only two Chemo treatments left. Mom and I even opened the conversation today about how we will celebrate. It is also ridiculous to see the end of Chemo as the end of this process.

There will be hormone therapy for five years and oncology visits for the rest of my life. I'm not clear on how they will be monitoring for recurrence or what the statistics are on whether I will ever face this again. I can hold my arms with hands up on each side of my body to create my own human scale. In any given moment, either side might be slightly heavier than the other, but all in all I am pretty balanced with my thinking. Happy and Cautious . . . I think it's a healthy balance.

Today was good. Good because I didn't respond as drastically to the meds. I did get dizzy but not as bad, and once I took a nap at home I was able to make some calls and answer some emails. I will not be getting as much antihistamine next time. They finally realized that I'm not very big, and I just don't need that much.

I guess today's theme for me is about paradox and balance. For a long time, I've been working hard to not be black and white in my thinking. There was certainly a time when, if I was happy, I couldn't (or wouldn't) consider anything that might go wrong. If I was scared or worried, it was too hard to see the brighter side or the possibilities. Oftentimes, my experience was to hold all the scary stuff inside and miraculously only show this great happy face to the rest of the world. What I find now is that it's healthiest for me to embrace, or at least accept, both. I allow myself to tip when it's time to tip, stay tipped if need be, and then consciously find my way back to that stable place that sits more in the middle.

Even knowing that a middle place exists has been big learning for me, and very intentional, in the past few years. I know I've said before how much I believe that everything we do sets us up or prepares us in some way for what will come next. This concept feels super real for me right now. I know in my blood and bones that I could never have maneuvered through the events of this year with any level of emotional health had it not been for so many things that I worked through before.

It's as though I'm taking a test in a class I didn't know I signed up for. I do hope I'm passing, and I can't help but wonder what Graduation will be like.

On another note, my hair really is growing! I was afraid it might fall out again, but it just might make it. It's about a quarter-inch long and very very very soft. The big mystery is what it will be like when it's full. Many people have told me that it could come back different: different texture, different color. Could be straight or could be curly. I thought it would all be white, but so far there is quite a bit of dark in the mix! This will be a fun mystery to see solved.

Saturday, August 7, 2010 7:55 AM, EDT

The past six months have all been about doing what had to be done, and there has clearly been a lot of loss in the process. One of the things I have not been able to do is to be on my bike, and that's been really, really hard to accept. What I want to help you understand is that for me it's about so much more than just riding. You see, it's on the bike where Scott and I get to spend what we consider to be our best quality time together. Our worlds are busy. He works long and hard hours and then goes non-stop with our own home renovation projects in the evenings and on weekends.

When I'm "healthy," I'm on the road over 100 days a year. Finding time to be together is no easy task. In our own right, we are both workaholics, and carving out time to play takes a lot of intention. Our tandem is our escape, part of our fitness, our social network, and a place where we can be together, laugh, and enjoy working toward a common goal. We've become a great team on our bike! When I say I miss riding, it's really about missing everything else that goes along with riding, too.

To put this in perspective, in a typical year we'd have 1,500 to 2,000 miles in the season by now. We'd be feeling very fit and geared up to do our "big rides." One of our events covers 100 miles in one day. Our goal is to average 20 miles per hour, and to complete it in just under five hours of riding time. Our other big ride is the MS fundraiser—150 miles in two days. This ride is extra special as it was our honeymoon ride fifteen years ago this month.

There are many other organized tours through the season that we typically enjoy, but this year has basically been a bust. We've ridden only a handful of times on the local bike trail. Even though we always enjoy riding with our friends, this has been a sad year to count miles. Instead, this season has been about breast reconstruction, Chemo, and Scott getting a ton of work done outside in the heat.

Since I'm feeling better through this last course of treatment, we've decided to do at least a portion of the MS fundraiser, and I am excited! So excited, in fact, that I took off on Monday to the MS headquarters to pick up our rider numbers and other stuff. A friend of mine decided to come along for the ride and off we went.

Before we left, I clearly remember thinking I had to get gas.

The weather was gorgeous, the top was down on the Mini Cooper, and great conversation filled the air. We made it out, picked up our stuff, and were on the way back. We were cruising down the highway without a care in the world, when all of a sudden, I had no more go-go. I pushed on the gas pedal and there was . . . nothing. Oh, crap! (This is the funny part.) I started to laugh immediately. Because I was in the fast lane, I started to merge over, popped into neutral, and was anxious to see how far I could coast. An exit was *right there*. In a perfect world, I could have made it over the off ramp and right into a gas station. Instead, I was about 500 feet shy of the exit and stopped with my hazard lights doing their job. I just couldn't stop laughing!

My girlfriend at this point was aware of how busy the highway was and got out of the car just in case somebody was stupid enough to hit us. I was busy calling Scott and the Mini Cooper roadside service for help. Next thing you know, a police car was pulling up in front of my poor flashing Mini. The officer was the nicest guy and offered to drive us up to a gas station to buy a can and some gas. Heck, it's been a while since I got to ride in the back of a police car. Why not? It seemed much faster than waiting for AAA.

As my girlfriend and I got into the back of the cruiser, our new friend, the police officer, told us that we needed to make a quick stop at his grandma's house. Seems he needed to drop his son off, who was also riding in the cruiser. At this point, I was still cracking myself up and becoming more and more aware of the fact that I wasn't the least bit upset. Okay, I felt a tiny bit bad, because I know that running out of gas is not good for my car, but the rest of me was the polar opposite of how I would have responded six months ago. I would have been nervous, mad at myself for being stupid, completely embarrassed, and probably anxious and frustrated.

Instead, here I was, heading for Grandma's house in the back of a cruiser, smiling at the whole thing.

When we dropped off the son in Grandma's driveway, I had this big idea. "Does Grandma by any chance have a gas can?" By golly, yes she did! Greg got out of the car, went into the garage, and emerged with a metal gas can that we learned was 36 years old. We borrowed the can, and he drove us to the gas station, pumped the gas, and then drove us back to my car with the now-full can plopped right on the front seat of the cruiser. I can't tell you how bad it smelled in that police car with the old can and stale cigarette smoke looming in the air. The important part is that we made it safe and sound back to my car, put in the two gallons of gas, and made our way safely back home.

My favorite part of this story is that I'm still laughing at myself about it. I guess once you've had your breasts removed and poison infused into your body over a period of months, your perspective on things can certainly change. Maybe I have learned a thing or two about what is important and what isn't. Maybe I'm not as worried about the "small stuff" as I used to be. And just maybe I've earned the right to do something really stupid and not beat myself up for it.

What I do know is that I have what I need to get on our bike next weekend with my captain of a husband, and that we will have a day or two of Being Normal on our bike. And oh, what an adventure it was to get our stuff!

Monday, August 16, 2010 9:14 PM, EDT

Every single day I continue to be amazed at my body: what it can do, can't do, and how it continues to change. There are days when I'm not even sure if the body I'm in belongs to me. What I'm most aware of in this moment is how surprised I am at the woman I see when I look in the mirror.

This weekend was our bike ride for MS, and it, too, was full of surprises. Scott and I love the spirit of community blended with the physical challenge and the bonus of raising money for a great cause. The first year I did this ride, I cried the last few miles. I guess it was a mixture of fatigue, relief, and pride. And then, at the very end, there were all these people, balloons, clapping, cheering, voices, yelling . . . and wheelchairs. So many people with MS, right there with their families and friends, thanking us. So many people were thanking us . . .

This year was different than usual in many ways. The most obvious difference was my own physical limitation. Instead of riding two days of 75 miles each, we rode one day of 41 miles. And it was hard. It was fun. It was hot. It was hard. It was great to see people we knew. I felt bad that

I couldn't do the whole thing, and I was really happy that I could do any of it at all. For all the cyclists out there, we averaged a respectable 18.3 miles per hour.

Other differences? For as many years as I can remember, my mom and dad would meet us at the lunch stop in Oberlin. It was the only time my folks ever got to see us on our bike, and that was fun for me. If you've ever been part of any fundraising or sporting event, you know how contagious the positive energy can be. Mom and Dad would enjoy being part of the scene for a little while, and it was great seeing them as we pulled in and then later rode away to complete our ride. Mom was so proud, and Dad would always say we needed a motor, and I would always tell him I *was* the motor.

This year, we began our ride at that rest stop in Oberlin. Mom and I never even talked about her coming out, because everything about our day was so not normal. But still, riding out of that rest stop was the first time I cried on Saturday. I miss my dad.

At the end of the ride, at Sandusky High School, I have a favorite tradition: I get a massage. There are a bunch of massage therapists who volunteer, and I always wait for Linda. She is a gifted therapist and also has MS. She's been working this event for twelve years as her way to show her gratitude to the National MS Society, and we enjoy our reunions year after year. Seeing Linda opened up the floodgates for me to have my next cry of the day. I found myself again feeling relief, fatigue, and pride, and all three were so much bigger and deeper than any year before. Scott had already told her about my "news," and she was literally standing with her arms open for me. Me, my sweaty self, and my little bald head fell into her arms.

One of the things that Linda and I noticed was significant swelling in my left arm, wrist, and hand. This was new, and more than a little scary. One of the potential effects from having lymph nodes removed is a condition called lymphedema. This had not been an issue for me since my surgery in March, so I figured I was in the clear. Maybe it was the heat. It was my longest ride of the year. Maybe it was from the pressure of my hand on the handlebars. Maybe it was a combination of all of the above. I looked something like the Pillsbury doughboy. Honestly, I just don't feel like dealing with another issue. I'll ask some questions at Cleveland Clinic tomorrow. Today it looks just fine.

In the meantime . . . tomorrow is number three of four of Round Two, number seven of a total of eight Chemo treatments. This is huge! I'm almost done. I'm really almost done. Except . . . I don't want to go tomorrow. Not at all. I kind of thought that as I got to the end, it would get easier. I figured the worst would be over and I'd cruise to the finish. For me, it's exactly the opposite. This is all a big mental game, and my mind is kicking and screaming as I get ready to "do it again." Yet "doing it again" is exactly what I will do.

I took my steroids, grabbed some cards from the basket, and am gearing up for what tomorrow and the days following will hold. This does feel very much like coming to the end of a long ride on my bike. I'm counting down the miles, working through the mental and physical challenges, and counting on Scott and all the people "riding" with us to help me remember that *I can do this.*

Hineni. Here I stand, continuing to move ahead still one step, one goal, one day at a time.

Screw the mirror. Puffy, bald, new boobage and no nipples. I'm still me.

Wish me luck!
Sheri

> This does feel very much like coming to the end of a long ride on my bike. I'm counting down the miles, working through the mental and physical challenges, and counting on Scott and all the people "riding" with us to help me remember that I can do this.

Chapter Seventeen
Layers and Complexities

Saturday, August 21, 2010 11:38 AM, EDT

This has been a really busy week and my mind seems to be working on overdrive. It would be easy to feel overwhelmed, so I'm doing my best to stay focused and concentrate on one thing at a time.

Chemo treatment number seven was on Tuesday, and it went really well. They gave me less antihistamine, which meant that even though I got tired, I didn't have to deal with the extreme dizziness and disorientation I had the last two times. That was good. The pain in my legs and feet was at its worst yesterday, but ibuprofen every couple of hours kept me functional, and I was able to attend a great lecture event with my team. I normally don't do a lot outside of my house on Chemo week, so I was really happy that it worked out for me to go. My energy was "good enough" and my pain was manageable.

Yesterday was also a significant day for another reason. Scott and I were celebrating our fifteenth wedding anniversary. We've been together since 1992, and memories of the past years have been flooding through like crazy. In retrospect, I notice that almost every conversation I've had this whole past week has been wrapped around the layers and complexities of relationships.

I've found myself in deep conversations with clients and friends about core concepts like values, intimacy, trust, personal needs, boundaries, growth, and change. I recognize more than ever how much intention and work it takes to co-create relationships that can sustain the dynamic nature of being together. I keep thinking about how unpredictable life is and how important it is to have key people in our lives that we can truly count on to be our touchstones toward sanity.

Especially when I'm in pain, I have a tendency to be emotional. Last night I was feeling a bit raw and at the same time very grateful to Scott for his love and support since my diagnosis. In my mind's eye, I took a trip back to the beginning of "us." I could feel the bumps and bruises along with the many moments of joy and laughter. As I touched down to land in the moment, one thing became crystal clear. I am not at all the woman Scott married. I've morphed and changed in every way: spiritually, emotionally, mentally, and, as I look in the mirror, especially physically.

All of a sudden I had this twinge of incredible insecurity. *Who had I become? And, most importantly, am I still a woman that he loves?*

My dear husband, who doesn't usually use many words, kindly responded with his own truth. He said that he is not the same person, either . . . and of course he loves me. Then we both agreed that we'd do it all over again if given the chance. Even though our relationship has not been easy, it certainly has been worth it. I know that because of one thing: I like who I am when I am with Scott. What a wonderful way to measure the quality of all my relationships.

I talk often about how much I've learned in the past year, since my diagnosis. As I sit here right now, I'm wondering to myself what has been most important in these lessons. Here's what I have for today.

Relationships are my lifeblood. They deserve to be treated with respect, honor, humility, and appreciation, and without judgment. I have never been more appreciative of my friends and family than I am right now. I literally could not have made it through this transformational time without you.

Each and every one of us influences those around us all the time, whether we intend to or not. It is my responsibility, my obligation, to do my best to have that influence be a positive one whenever possible. I believe that I must take responsibility for my own actions. At the very least, I must become aware of how I may be impacting others.

Life is uncertain. I will no longer wait to do anything that is really important to me. My bucket list will constantly be evolving.

It's okay to be scared. Doing things that frighten me helps me realize my own potential. No fear, no challenge, no growth, no learning.

Every minute of every day, I have the ability to make choices. I also have the prerogative to change my mind. Life is one giant experiment of choices. I will continue to live my life from a place of love and gratitude.

I hope your day is filled with at least one thing to be grateful for. Mine certainly is.

> Love,
> Sheri

Tuesday, August 31, 2010 8:37 PM, EDT

Refreshing, new, selfish, and perfect

It's hard to put into words what it is like to be on the downhill slope after climbing such a huge and frightening mountain. Knowing that my last treatment is just around the corner is filling me with a sense of freedom and very deep relief. What I am finding more than anything is that each and every day is incredibly important to me.

One of my most brilliant decisions as of late was to postpone my final Chemo until after Labor Day. Mostly, I wanted to feel good for the holiday weekend, and as a bonus, I was able to work out a business trip to the Florida Keys. I am writing this entry from my hotel room on Duck Key, where I am staying at a beautiful resort. I came in a day early so that I could have the afternoon to sit by the pool and do as much "nothing" as possible. And you know what? I *loved* doing nothing! I slathered on sunscreen, swam a bit, read a lot, made a couple of calls, and rested.

I also really wanted to do something else. I had seen on the Internet that there were dolphins here. Even though I'd had an incredible experience with wild dolphins a few years ago, I'd always wanted to be a bit more up close and personal with them. When I checked into the resort, I inquired about their programs but was told that it wouldn't work out, and I let it go. A few hours later, I was on the phone with the team I'm here to work with. It just so happens that one of their patients works here, and you can guess how it went. A couple of phone calls later, I was signing waivers and getting ready to do this thing!

The best part? I was the only person working with the trainers and the dolphins! They usually do groups of eight or ten people at a time and usually only spend about twenty minutes in the water.

The trainers were a joy to be with. I got to spend almost an hour with five different dolphins—my new friends. I got to rub them and swim with them and hug them and shake "hands." I laughed like a little kid and cried like a baby. We joked that this was like a Make-A-Wish Foundation event for me. And it really was. (By the way, I think it sucks that they don't have that for adults.)

This was one more thing I'd always wanted to do, and the experience was pure joy. I didn't care about the cost and I didn't care that I was alone. Historically, I don't do anything alone. Half the fun of doing anything has been doing whatever it was with somebody else. Today was refreshing, new, selfish, and perfect. The trainers asked me more than once if there was somebody to watch. I'm still so surprised at myself that having somebody wasn't important at all. I absolutely loved the "doing it" part!

So today was amazing and today was magical. Today really mattered. From the moment I left the airport and saw the ocean, I knew today would be special. It's not like I think that every day for the rest of my life will be like today, nor would I want it to be. What I do think is that more days can have at least a little more magic. After all, I'm almost done doing the hardest thing I've ever done. Each day is a new reward, and I hope and pray that I never forget what it took to get me here.

> Each day is a new reward, and I hope and pray that I never forget what it took to get me here.

I end this day filled with joy and gratitude.

Love to you,
Sheri

Saturday, September 4, 2010 8:43 AM, EDT

Ready to kiss
Cancer good-bye

This picture is obviously from my dolphin adventure the other day. I'm posting it today as I prepare for Tuesday, my last Chemo, when I am officially *kissing Cancer good-bye*. In my mind, after Chemo, there is literally only one thing left, and that is when I have my port surgically removed on September 27.

Many people are asking me what comes next and how I will know I really am Cancer-free. The answer to both questions lies physiologically in follow-up blood work that will occur every few months at first, and then annually after the first year. For me, the answer also lives in my Spirit and soul as I continue to picture my body as healthy and "clean." My reality is coming out of my mouth in conversations almost daily when I hear myself say, "I am so done." I am emotionally done with treatment, done with being bald, done with my feet and legs hurting, done with feeling like a puffer fish, and done with being the face of Cancer.

I am only two very small steps away from everything else. I look at my future every day, celebrating the fact that I have one. It's also important that I say out loud that I am not stupid and I am not in denial about the fact that recurrence is possible. I can also get hit by a bus tomorrow. None of us have any guarantees. All of us have choices, though, about what we do with each present moment. My choice right now is to celebrate!

Let's have a party! On Saturday, September 18, there will be a potluck at our house to celebrate life.

If you are reading this, you are invited. If you know somebody who might not be reading this, they are also invited. We *all* have something to celebrate, right?

The evening will be full of fun, as we have no idea how many people will come or who will surprise us. Just like life: we never know exactly what will happen, no matter how hard we try to plan. I might as well just "let it unfold" and see how it goes.

Love to you,
Sheri

Thursday, September 9, 2010 8:35 PM, EDT

My last Chemo on Tuesday— here I am with one of my angels at the Cleveland Clinic.

My guess would have been that I'd be bouncing off the walls with happiness this week as I completed my eighth and final Chemo. It certainly does feel good and I am happy . . . just not bouncing. Thinking back, it has been as if each treatment carried its own energy and experience along with it. I remember fear, anxiety, calm, and even boredom at some points. This last treatment holds a story of its own, as I gently and slowly attempt to close such a difficult chapter in this book.

Along with this week being my last treatment, this is also the week of Rosh Hashanah, the Jewish New Year. According to Judaism, this is the time of year when God makes some pretty big decisions. As the story goes, God inscribes in the Book of Life "who shall live and who shall die." It is also a time of reflection for each of us about the past year. This holiday creates the opportunity to ask forgiveness for any sins we may have committed.

By now, you know me well enough to know that I am quite naturally a "reflective" individual. As I raise the intention of reflection even higher in the midst of this holiday, I find myself feeling quite melancholy. After all . . . it's been one hell of a hard year.

If somebody would have asked me one year ago today what I envisioned happening in the next twelve months, I don't think I would have told a story even close to what actually occurred. My reflections take me to feelings of wonder, sadness, and gratitude. I consider this past year much as I would a dream I can't fully recall, the feelings all real and touchable, the details incredibly foggy.

What is clear, and has always been clear throughout this year, is the steady and unwavering show of support that has been coming my way. I continue to be humbled by the generosity of so many who have gone so far above and beyond, over and over again. I once again thank each of you and make my promise that I will continue to "pay it forward" in any way I can for the rest of my life.

I close today with my official good-bye to the year . . . and to Cancer. I envision the year ahead as one filled with health, healing, and an abundance of love and community.

I love you, Mom. I miss you, Daddy.

Sheri

Chapter Eighteen
Do I Want to Be the Same?

For everything there is a season, and a time for every purpose under heaven:

> I can feel so many things coming full circle, so many beginnings now finding their end.

a time to be born, and a time to die; a time to plant, and a time to pluck up that which is planted;

> Remember that I got my diagnosis this past February while I was in Guatemala for a mission trip? I just sent in my application to go back again in February 2011. Life goes on.

a time to kill, and a time to heal; a time to break down, and a time to build up;

> One year ago today, I was recovering from a very invasive breast biopsy and was considering prophylactic mastectomies. We can't live in regret.

a time to weep, and a time to laugh; a time to mourn, and a time to dance;

> Also one year ago, one of my very dearest friends was seemingly losing her battle with a brain tumor. A miracle happened and she is still alive and doing remarkably well. I love you, Jane.

a time to cast away stones, and a time to gather stones together; a time to embrace, and a time to refrain from embracing;

> This has been a time of huge growth as I opened my heart and learned to truly receive. Kindness has been the most powerful medicine.

a time to seek, and a time to lose; a time to keep, and a time to cast away;

> This year reminded me over and over again what is really important and what is not. Love, community, tears, and laughter are the things that make us human.

a time to rend, and a time to sew; a time to keep silence, and a time to speak;

> It has taken me my entire lifetime to learn that my voice of self-care and acceptance can be louder and stronger than the inner critic that has been screaming so loudly in my head for as long as I can remember. I am enough. I am whole.

a time to love, and a time to hate; a time for war, and a time for peace.

> Today I feel complete. Full. Done. Loved. Thankful.
>
> And so it is . . . I am still me . . .
>
> *Hineni.*

Sunday, September 26, 2010 6:19 PM, EDT

It's been a while since I took time to write, and it feels important to check in today as I prepare to have my port removed tomorrow. My emotions seem to be all mixed up, so I thought it might be helpful to pound them out on my keyboard.

Let me think about this for a minute, 'cause there is a lot going on in here . . . I've got:

> *Happy*
> *Relieved*
> *Scared*
> *Confident*
> *Loved*
> *Excited*
> *and very, very Raw and Open*

Now, what if I dig a little deeper?

Happy . . . to be alive, plain and simple. These past nine months have been a test of all that makes me a whole, vital person, and I am happy not only to be alive, but also to have a plan to live a long and joyful life.

Relieved . . . that so much is behind me instead of in front of me. I remember having to break down the Chemo rounds to two groups of four when facing eight was too much to handle. I recall fearing so much of the unknown about surgeries and therapies and wondering whether or not I could still work or enjoy food. I can still touch the anxiety that came with having the surgical markings drawn on my breasts the day before surgery. Wow, that seems like a long time ago. On a scale of one to ten, I feel relief at an eleven that we have come so far.

Scared . . . of ever having to face this again and scared to find out how "this" will continue to impact me as I move forward and away from Cancer. There are two questions that I am asking myself over and over that will probably keep my mind and heart busy for a while. As a result of this experience, How am I the same and how am I different? And then I go to another place. How do I *want* to be the same and how do I *want* to be different?

These questions both scare and inspire me. I once again go to a place of choice. I have not been and will never be a victim of Cancer. I am instead a student of life, and Cancer has indeed been a very powerful teacher. Maybe I'm scared of what it means to have lost what was left of my innocence, or my naiveté, or my illusions of predictability.

Confident . . . that there is life past and beyond Cancer, and that my relationships with the most significant people in my life will continue to be my strength and my joy. I am also more confident in myself than I have ever been. I have made good choices, informed decisions, and have done my best to stay focused and productive. If I can do "this," I can do almost anything.

Loved . . . I have always felt Love in my life, yet I have never felt the depth or intensity of Love the way I have since my diagnosis. I have been surprised over and over at the many different ways that my friends and family have demonstrated how they feel, and I again thank you all and continue to be humbled by your generosity.

Excited... about what the future holds! I'm not going to say that every tree is more green or every flower more beautiful, but I will tell you that I hold more moments as precious. Yes, I hold more moments as precious. My tolerance for the trivial is diminishing, and my expectations of myself are certainly different as I renew my beliefs about what is most important.

I am excited about what every tomorrow will bring. This entire year has been one of literal survival. My heart and Spirit have been opened in ways that were new and unfamiliar. As I move into the strategic ending of having my port removed tomorrow, I am also left not knowing how to process, manage, and work through the emotional components that still so fully exist. I trust that gaining the closure I seek will be yet another evolving process. It's not like saying good-bye to an old and dear friend I invited to spend a weekend. This is more like figuring out how to lovingly pick up all the pieces of a shattered glass, with shards skipping and hiding beyond my view. At this point in time, I'm not sure when I'll be walking barefoot in my room and surprised as I step on yet another sliver.

Tomorrow should be easy. They will use a local to numb the area, make a two-inch incision, and remove the port and catheter. They will then stitch me up and send me on my way. Isn't it crazy? This little port that I named Polly so many months ago. The little alien that lived in my chest and showed for all the world to see. This vehicle for Chemo, this direct line to make me healthy again.

"'Bye, Polly. I thank you and I won't miss you. I won't need you ever again because . . . I am done!"

Love to you all,
Sheri

Tuesday, October 5, 2010 12:22 PM, EDT

Who is this woman?

Once upon a time, and it does seem like a long, long time ago, there lived a happy woman. She had a full head of wavy thick hair, near-perfect dark eyebrows, and long and lush eyelashes . . . what the hell? Who needs hair, anyway?

I really thought I was going to squeak by! My eyebrows and eyelashes put up a damned good fight since the hair on my head and nearly every other strand of hair on my body disappeared. My Chemo finished a month ago today, and just in the past ten days or so, it's gotten to where I can count the little feisty remainders of eyelashes on one hand.

I'm not really upset about it. In the grand scheme of the world, it's just not such a big deal to be without either my brows or my lashes. In the beginning, I was literally praying that I would keep them. My thinking then was that I could still pull off looking somewhat healthy if my brows and lashes were intact. I do believe that it is the loss of those that makes people look "sick." It's just that by now I'm feeling better on the inside, so it doesn't so much matter about the outside.

My only real complaint is that what little lashes I have are short and pokey in my poor eyeballs. Does that make any sense? Oh well, it will all grow back, right? Actually, I think it would be way fun if I could have a checklist of where I do and do not want hair to grow back! We could call it a consolation prize after such a big mess of a year. And with whom might I speak about such a request? Fine, I'll move on.

At least the hair on my head is happily sprouting! I even had some downright unruly ones, so I asked Scott to pull out the clippers the other night just so we could even things out a bit. I'm sure my poor little follicles have been confused ever since I stopped Chemo in the middle for my reconstruction. During the final four treatments, it seemed as though my little hairs kept coming and then going again. My thinking is that my hair is finally finding that it's safe to go for the gusto and fight its way back to fullness.

I also want to let you know that last Monday I did indeed say good-bye to Polly. The procedure itself was just what I expected, and very easy. Although I was at the Clinic for almost two hours with pre-op and post-op stuff, the actual technical piece was fifteen minutes start to finish. I got numb, Polly was easily removed, and my favorite surgeon stitched me up. Because I have developed quite the allergy to any bandages, they used this super-glue stuff, and I must say I looked pretty Frankenstein-ish for the week. I also had a bit of a surprise.

You may remember that I had been thinking a lot about the idea of closure. I knew that the port removal would indeed provide me with the strategic side of ending treatment, but I was also really working many angles of what might help me on the spiritual and emotional sides of closure. I was thinking about asking my friends to help me with some kind of ceremony, maybe a fire, or drumming, or maybe some writing, or a combination of many things. What I did not expect was that I would have so much closure occur on so many levels last Monday.

As soon as the doctor told me that the port was out, a few tears began to fall. When he was completely done, he asked if I wanted to see it. To set the context a bit more, for the entire procedure my head was turned to the left, where I was staring at a whiteboard in the surgery room. It said:

> September 27, 2010
> Sheri Kay
> Port removal / Right side

I must have read that board a hundred times as I allowed my mind to weave back through the events of the year. I became aware of so many events, conversations, other surgeries, decisions, thoughts and feelings, fears and celebrations that have occurred since January. And I just kept staring at the words—only this is what my mind was seeing:

Today
I
Make it end

Many people suggested that I keep the port in for at least a year following my Chemo. This was one thing I could control, one piece I could decide about. I needed that damned thing out. Inside and outside of me, I no longer wanted to be an open vessel for more treatment. Although I have many reminders in any given moment of what Cancer has done in and to my body, Polly in her own way was more than a reminder. She was "alive" and waiting for more. I wanted no part of that thinking.

When the doctor showed me the port and tubing, all I could do was take a deep breath and take in all that Polly represented. I laugh now, thinking that after nine months, maybe she became part of some birthing process I don't yet fully understand.

Anyway, it was just after he left the room that the tears really began to flow. The nurses were so kind, and although I don't remember exactly what was said, I do remember hearing, "Sweetie, it's okay to cry; you have been through so much."

All of a sudden, as if for the first time, I felt just how much my body and Spirit have endured.

It was certainly a flood that came next, and for the next two days I could cry in almost any moment. I have no doubt that as the port came out, so did zillions of bound-up

I do remember hearing,
"Sweetie,
it's okay to cry;
you have been
through so much."

All of a sudden,
as if for the
first time,
I felt just
how much
my body
and Spirit
have endured.

emotions, fears, and who knows what else that was hiding in there that would no longer serve me. I experienced a huge release within my Spirit, and in many ways I feel that I also regained some pieces of me that may have been lost along this journey. I am sure that my healing and more layers of closure will continue to flow over a long period of time. I also believe, at least for now, that the biggest piece is behind me.

Today, even though my mirror may show a different image, I feel perfectly "whole." At least for today, screw the mirror! Over time, I am quite hopeful that what's going on with my outsides will catch up to what is going on with my insides.

Love to you all,
Sheri

Every time your heart leaps out and you want to serve better,
that's the future speaking through you.
——Margaret Wheatley

Chapter Nineteen
The End of "This"

Wednesday, October 27, 2010 7:43 PM, EDT

My eyebrows are
coming back,
and my face is red
from a hot flash.

I've been getting more calls and emails than usual to see how I'm doing, and it made me realize that it's been a really long time since I wrote!

In a nutshell, life is being good to me. It still feels like I'm playing "catch up" from the year, and I'm enjoying the emotional stability that a full schedule provides. The other edge of that sword is that I still get more tired than I expect. It's almost funny that I have to remind myself that I'm still recovering. As much as I want to believe that "it" is over, I'm honestly not sure that "this" has an ending.

My recent conversations and thoughts have been around recognizing and coming to terms with my early delusions that this Cancer process had three parts: a beginning, a middle, and an end. I was right about the beginning and the middle. I can touch, see, and feel those parts. The delusion is all about the ending. Please don't hear this as anything morbid, but rather as perfectly pragmatic. I have no idea what the end of "this" will look like, physically or emotionally.

Here is what I know now about my physicality. I still have significant foot, leg, and hand pain. The worst part is my hands, and I'm grateful that performing as a dental hygienist is not how I currently earn my keep. Hot flashes are part of my days and nights, and I'm searching for that magic herb or tea that will make them stop or at least calm down. I still get tired. My theory is that this is all still post-Chemo stuff, although my oncologist does not agree.

I also still have a lot of swelling that comes and goes. None of this is life threatening or even a quality-of-life issue . . . just subtle reminders of where I have been. (Now, if these are still present for next year's cycling season, I will be majorly pissed.)

Which brings me to the spiritual/emotional side of "this." I am most aware of an overall sense of both freedom and calm. As long as I can remember, I've carried a pretty high level of anxiety around with me like an old friend. All of a sudden, I realized that if I could make it through the past nine months with any level of grace, I can do almost anything. And, I don't have to get all crazy about stuff.

I still love, remain passionate about almost anything that's in front of me, and am looking forward to many new adventures. I can't wait to try new things, embrace new learning, and make new friends. What I don't have to do is allow or encourage any day-to-day drama that serves no higher purpose. I finally, really get the whole idea of "life's too short."

The only buzz of anxiety that I do still carry has to do with the uncertainties of tomorrow and my not-so-hidden wants. This buzz resonates at a very low frequency down deep in my soul and carries a gentleness, a lightness. It's the wondering about how my body will respond to Tamoxifen, which will be prescribed to me next week. It's the fear that my hands will still hurt next summer. It's my knowing that things can change in an instant, with me or with somebody I love or care about. It's my desire to be a better listener, a more appreciative wife, a more attentive daughter, sister, mother, and friend. It's my trust that I have been put on this earth for a reason and that each day is part of my destiny.

Today I am seven weeks post-Chemo and happy that I get to sleep in my own bed tonight.

Today I loved working from my living room with my dog curled up by my side.

Today I embrace the sense of feeling Whole and Grounded.

Today was good.

Saturday, November 13, 2010 10:36 AM, EST

Sporting the new look

Bring it on! The time has come for shaving and tweezing and waxing once again. Welcome, Hair! I never really thought about how happy I could be to put a fresh blade in my razor after not much needing it for six months. Razor stubble rocks!

About three weeks ago, I decided that I had enough hair on my head for me to start going more in public without a hat or scarf. It has been nicely liberating, although I must admit that it has taken me a while to actually feel confident with this new look that I'm sporting.

Wearing something on my head has been quite paradoxical in that I was both hiding and highlighting the effects of Chemo at the same time. I never got to the point where I was perfectly unmindful of or comfortable with not having hair, and I also was more tired than I can tell you of having my head wrapped in scarves or putting on a hat. It was a hot summer, and I've never been one to like anything "constricting."

When I look in the mirror now, what I see is really short hair. What I don't see is what I used to call the "face of Cancer." My hair is full enough that my scalp isn't peeking through, and it honestly feels fuller almost every day, especially yesterday. You'll love this one.

While I was on a business trip to Atlanta, I was staying at a friend's house. There were a number of bottles on the shower shelf, and it took me a minute without my glasses to identify what was what. I found the body wash, face scrub, more face wash, and finally, exactly what I was looking for: volumizing shampoo! It only takes about a pea-sized amount of shampoo for me to work up a lather, and I just couldn't stop laughing. If you could see me now, you would have to laugh, too, 'cause the giggles won't stop about this even as I type. Sometimes I just crack myself up.

The other thing that has been putting a smile on my face the past few days is how people are responding to me. Strangers, I mean real strangers, are somehow compelled to make comments, compliments about my "cool, New York chic" look. One guy (okay, he was kinda old, overweight, and sweaty . . . but still) stopped me at a hotel last week to say, "Nice hair! Very sexy!" He had this big smile on his face, and I couldn't help but smile back and simply say, "Thanks."

Physical update: a prescription anti-inflammatory is helping my hands and feet, and as a result my workouts are staying steady. My strength and energy continue to improve, and I'm being really good about eating healthy. For me, that means very little (if any) flour or sugar 90 percent of the time, and as much water and whole food as possible.

Every day is a blessing, and I love looking for reasons to smile and laugh.

> Love to you,
> Sheri

Sunday, November 21, 2010 8:11 PM, EST

It became clear to me a long time ago that nothing in life is static. In fact, my own experience continues to challenge the idea that any level of predictability exists. What I'm learning to embrace is that almost everything I can think of is perfectly dynamic. Ironically, I've been talking to my clients and teams for years about this very thing, and I'm still having a "hit myself in the forehead" moment as I apply this thinking to me.

Let's take happiness, for example, or health, or success. All of these things can be touched. All of these things can be felt. It seems to me that these dynamic "things" live on a continuum of sorts and, if we are interested, it's our job to simply pay attention to where on the line we would plot them for ourselves. In any given moment, I can ask myself this question: "Am I moving closer to or further away from what I want?"

For example, if *health* is my goal and I'm not sure if I have the motivation to work out, or not eat a cookie, all I have to do is ask this magical question. In any given moment, I can be certain of only one thing: my decisions will most certainly influence whether I am moving *toward* or *away* from whatever *it* is.

For the few weeks prior to starting on Tamoxifen, I experienced a lot of anxiety about taking the drug. To be honest, I was having a negative visceral response that felt disproportionately huge in light of already having gone through major surgeries and Chemo. I mean, what was the big deal for me about taking a little pill once a day for a few years? I was rationally nervous about potential side effects, but there was more to it that I couldn't put my finger on, until now.

This little pill that is supposed to be taken at the same time every day is my reminder. My reminder of what has been and my reminder of what can still be. This little pill is an unreliable insurance policy designed to minimize the risk of ever having to go through what I and we have already been through. I embrace and resent everything it represents— and if I want this little pill to be most effective, I need to be aware of it at about the same time every single day for the next few years.

Scott and I talked a lot about my decision process, because not taking Tamoxifen was also an option. He was his usual, amazing, supportive self, and reminded me that I could do anything I wanted, including not taking it. He also reminded me of our very early conversations when I fully committed to be as aggressive as possible. Words resonated in my head and heart from an old patient of mine who was conservative with her treatment a decade ago and has now been battling a stage-four recurrence in her chest wall. We spoke early in my process and she said over and over to me, "Be aggressive." She significantly influenced my initial decision to fight fast and hard, so that down the road, I would have no regrets about my choices.

In the end, it all came down to one simple question: could Tamoxifen, even potentially, take me closer or further away from my desired outcome?

As I ponder other life choices, I'm finding it so helpful to look at the bigger picture and be mindful about how they may impact the core life values that I hold so dear. I do want health. I do want to be happy. I do want to be successful. I am also 100 percent certain that life has more than a few more curveballs to throw in my direction. My job is to remain intimately aware and hold myself responsible and accountable for how I respond along the way. I won't be perfect, and some of my choices will take me away. That's okay, too. For me, the beauty lies in the choices that will come after that, and after that, and after that.

In terms of an update, I have been on the medication for a few weeks now. The hot flashes could roast marshmallows, and I seem to be retaining some fluid. That's it, other than remembering to take that little pill at 9 o'clock every night. And so it is . . .

Wednesday, November 24, 2010 5:28 PM, EST

Grateful for the energies of family

Of the many things I have to be grateful for, one of the most significant is all about family. I actually feel a little spoiled, because I know that some people don't have a family at all, while I have so many I am deeply connected to. For me, Thanksgiving started this past weekend with one of my most special families.

My decision to go should have been hard, since my calendar was already back-to-back travel for the entire month of November. On the other hand, it would have been impossible to say "no" to joining in on the fun for a super-secret surprise birthday party when I heard the entire family would be there. Before I knew it, I was changing around my travel plans and sneaking in a detour to Scottsdale, Arizona.

There are many people I care a lot about who live really far away, and I'm often aware of how much I miss them. What tickles my soul is that when we actually are together, I realize just how much I have missed them and how much I love being with them.

My heart was singing the whole time we were together. It was fun to be immersed in the energies of babies and laughing and bumps on the heads. I was warmed by conversations about the past and inspired by ones about the future. I have known this family for sixteen years, and I loved being surrounded by each and all of them.

As I've been anticipating this Thanksgiving, my feelings have been bittersweet. I do, I do, I do have so much to be Thankful for.

Especially since my diagnosis, there has not been a single day that I didn't spend time intentionally thinking about what I have to be grateful for. I love Thanksgiving, the perfect holiday: a day to sleep in, watch parades on TV, eat great food, enjoy family and friends, and have no pressure about anything like presents. All this is still true, except this year, Thanksgiving is also about missing part of our family. I'm not sure I know how to have Thanksgiving without my dad.

I think about my dad every day, and as this holiday has been creeping closer, I've been missing him more and more. I think that's why the timing was so beautifully perfect for me to be with this family this past weekend. At one point, I had one of those big emotional waves sneak up on me so fast I hardly knew what hit me. And as only a family could do,

144

one person held me, and then another . . . No one even asked why. It felt so good to be hugged while I had a good cry. Eventually, the family's grown son popped over and asked if we were playing "pass the Sheri." We certainly were, and I felt so safe in each person's arms.

I'm a lucky girl to have this and other special families. Little pieces of my Spirit live all around the world. My arms stretch across the map as I wrap them around all the members of my families that live in the many circles of my life.

This Thanksgiving, there will be just a few of us sitting at the table, and more than one chair will be almost unbearably empty. I'm reminding myself how important it is to hold "the both." The both of feeling loved and alone. The both of feeling full and empty. The both of feeling grateful and full of grief.

To all of my family, my mom, my sisters, my brother, my husband, my kids, my extended family, and my friends:

I am Thankful and Grateful.

I Love and Appreciate each and all of you.

Many blessings to you today and every day.

I love and miss you, Daddy.

Chapter Twenty
Embracing the Both

Monday, December 6, 2010 9:10 PM, EST

For as long as I can remember, December has been a month when everything slows down. You know, the trees are all naked and the bears go off to hibernate somewhere. All of us two-leggeds settle into the cold and wait for the snow. This year, December feels completely different, and I feel as though I'm running into it and gaining speed along the way. I'm sure it's the hot flashes, but the cold (and it is very cold out there) isn't even fazing me. I love the brisk freshness in the air and the anticipation of the New Year right around the corner. I don't know that I've ever been so happy about a year coming to a close.

Once again, I find myself embracing the both, but this time it is the both of endings and new beginnings. After all, you can't have one without the other.

Two months ago, I was giving a lot of thought and energy to what closure would look like for me after all the surgeries and Chemo. I wasn't sure what "life after Cancer" would look like, and I certainly won't pretend that I've gotten all my answers. What has happened, though, is that I am really starting to feel more and more like the "me" that I remember before my diagnosis. There is an easiness about my being that feels both new and familiar, and an energy inside me that is both growing and steady.

There is also a sense of groundedness that is deep and centered and balanced in a way that I never knew could exist in my Spirit.

I've been able to answer many levels of the questions *How am I the same?* and *How am I different?* I hope I remember to keep asking myself those same questions for the rest of my very long life.

It was exactly one year ago when I called to schedule my mammogram for January. The entire *flunk my mammogram, have a sonogram, then a biopsy, then mastectomies, then Chemo and blah blah blah* cycle began.

Now here we are in December, and my insides are celebrating that this cycle is really over.

December is monumental!

December is the capstone!

I celebrate December of 2010 as the month I leap out of fear, fatigue, and baldness.

When I look in the mirror, I no longer see the face of Cancer. I see the face of a grateful woman who was held up for a year by a devoted husband, an amazing mother, and the best friends and family anyone could ever dream of.

I see Hope.

I see Faith.

I see endless possibilities.

Here is my final *Hineni!*

I am here with all of my being, physically and spiritually, ready to do what I need to do and fully present in the moment.

This will most likely be my last formal post . . . although I just may surprise you every once in a while with a quick update or just to say hello. I send you love and light, and once again I humbly thank you for your love and support. I could not have done this without you.

Love to you all,
Sheri

When I look in the mirror, I no longer see the face of Cancer. I see the face of a grateful woman who was held up for a year by a devoted husband, an amazing mother, and the best friends and family anyone could ever dream of.
I see Hope.
I see Faith.
I see endless possibilities.

For More Information:

Sheri Kay
www.SheriKay.com
sherikay.hineni@gmail.com

Chapter One:
Latin American Medical Providers (LAMP)
578 Sunset Ridge Road
Northfield, IL 60093
www.LampCharity.org

Chapter Twelve:
R. Scott Brooks
Continuation: Honoring and Celebrating the Human Condition
Eugene: Continuation Publishing Group, 2001
www.continuationbook.com

Chapter Sixteen:
National MS Society "Bike MS" events
www.ms150.org
www.nationalmssociety.org

Chapter Seventeen:
The Make-A-Wish Foundation
www.wish.org

Hawk's Cay, Florida
www.HawksCay.com